D1406393

Ludwig van Beethoven

FOURTH AND FIFTH SYMPHONIES

in Full Orchestral Score

Ludwig van Beethoven

FOURTH AND FIFTH SYMPHONIES

in Full Orchestral Score

Dover Publications, Inc., New York

This Dover edition, first published in 1976, reproduces all the music from the separate volumes of the symphonies edited by Max Unger and published by Ernst Eulenburg, Ltd., London, n.d. (the Editor's Preface to the Fourth Symphony is dated 1938). In the present volume, the introductions by Wilhelm Altmann (in the Eulenburg volumes these are in their original German with French and English translations) are reproduced in English only—but in a totally new translation—while the Editor's Preface *(Revisionsbericht)* to the Fourth Symphony, originally in German only, also appears in a specially prepared new English translation.

International Standard Book Number: 0-486-23378-2
Library of Congress Catalog Card Number: 76-12890

Manufactured in the United States of America
Dover Publications, Inc.
180 Varick Street
New York, N.Y. 10014

Contents

Symphony No. 4 in B-flat Major, Op. 60

The original score, presented by Messrs. Mendelssohn-Bartholdy in 1908 to the Music Division of the Prussian State Library in Berlin, is titled: "Sinfonia 4ta 1806 L. v. Bthvn."

The sketches for this B-flat major symphony are apparently lost. The work was begun after Beethoven had already started the C minor symphony in 1805 or even 1804. In a letter of September 3, 1806, he already offered it along with other works to the Leipzig publishing house of Breitkopf & Härtel, but this does not mean it was completed. At the time, Beethoven was at Prince Lichnowsky's country seat Grätz near Troppau. On September 13 the publishers asked what payment he wanted. Beethoven did not reply until November 18; in the meantime he had been negotiating with the London publisher George Thomson concerning the sale of his new works in England, and wanted to grant Breitkopf & Härtel only the exclusive rights for Germany. He wrote: "I cannot yet give you the promised symphony, because a distinguished gentleman has taken it from me, though I have the liberty to publish it in half a year. . . . It may be possible for me to have the symphony engraved sooner than I was given to hope previously, and then you can have it right away."

This distinguished gentleman cannot have been Count Franz von Oppersdorff (château near Ober-Glogau in Upper Silesia), to whom this B-flat major symphony was dedicated when printed;[1] rather, it was Prince von Lobkowitz, who had it performed in March 1807.

The negotiations with Breitkopf & Härtel[2] broke off, as did those with the Parisian publisher Ignaz Pleyel, to whom Beethoven had written on April 26, 1807. On the other hand, he sold his Fourth Symphony at the same time to the London music publisher Muzio Clementi. The publication for Germany appeared first, in parts, during March of 1809.[3]

The publishing house was the Vienna Kunst- und Industrie-Kontor, headed by the theater manager Joseph Schreyvogel. According to Beethoven's letter of June or July 1807 to Ignaz von Gleichenstein, the composer had already sent the symphony to Schreyvogel by that time. The exact title of the first edition reads: "IVme Sinfonie à 2 Violins, Alto, Flûte, 2 Hautbois, 2 Clarinettes, 2 Cors, 2 Bassons, Trompettes, Timbales, Violoncelle et Basse. Composée et dediée à Monsieur le Comte Oppersdorff par Louis van Beethoven. OEuvre 60. A Vienne et Pesth au Bureau des arts et d'industrie" (publication number 596).

The first edition of the score was not published until 1821[4] (N. Simrock, Bonn, publication number 2078).

Beethoven did not add the metronome marks till later, at the same time as those for Symphonies 1 through 3 and 5 through 8; all these were published in the supplement to the *Allgemeine musikalische Zeitung*, Leipzig, of December 17, 1817.

WILHELM ALTMANN

---

1 This Count Oppersdorff did commission a symphony from Beethoven, and must have had a little misunderstanding with him, to judge by an undated letter of Beethoven's (Thayer-Deiters-Riemann, II, p. 11): "I will . . . only inform you that your symphony has long been ready, and I am sending it to you by the next mail. . . . In case you do not want the symphony, let me know before the next mailing day—but in case you take it, then delight me as soon as possible with the 300 gulden still due to me.—The last movement has 3 trombones and a piccolo—to be sure, this is not 3 drums, but will make more noise than 6 drums, and better noise." Therefore the symphony in question here is the Fifth, in C minor. We read further in Beethoven's letter to Count Oppersdorff of November 1, 1808: "You will regard me in a false light, but necessity compelled me to sell the symphony written for you and another one besides [the "Pastoral"] to someone else—but be assured that you will soon receive the one intended for you."

2 When Beethoven, in a letter of July 16, 1808 (he was then negotiating with them over the Fifth and Sixth Symphonies), told Breitkopf & Härtel that they could have yet another symphony, and within four weeks at most, he could only have had the Fourth in mind; but instead he sent the two piano trios Op. 70, because in the meantime he had made a different decision about publishing the Fourth, or else had not been able to get it back from its then owner, i.e., the man who had commissioned it.

3 Not 1808, as in Thayer-Deiters-Riemann. The Fourth Symphony was announced as a new publication (as were the Fifth and Sixth) in the news sheet of the *Allgemeine musikalische Zeitung* of April 1809 (p. 51).

4 It was not announced in the news sheet of the *Allgemeine musikalische Zeitung* until March 1826, together with the scores of the first three symphonies.

Editor's Preface to Fourth Symphony

My basic texts for editing this symphony were a photocopy of the original autograph MS (this photocopy is in the Master Archive of the Vienna National Library) and the copy of the first printing of the parts preserved in Hans C. Bodmer's Beethoven collection in Zurich. Neither of these two texts has an unusual number of errors in the musical notes, and both are fairly well provided with expression marks; ties and slurs were handled the least carefully. The autograph MS was obviously not used as the engraving copy, since aside from various confusing corrections entered by the composer, the customary engraver's notations are lacking. The engraving copy, presumably prepared by a copyist, is probably lost. In this Preface I have tacitly omitted mention of the divergences from the first printing and the MS wherever it was a matter of unmistakable error, and have tacitly supplied dynamic and expression marks that were clearly lacking.

First Movement

Mm. 26 & 27 (p. 3): In the MS and first-edition parts, the 2nd violins do not have quarter-notes: 

but instead eighth-notes with eighth-rests:

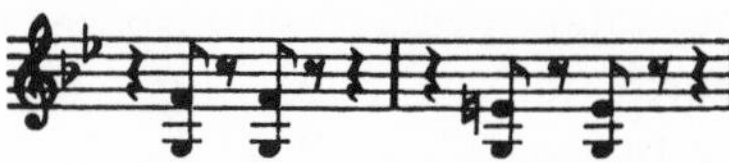

A comparison with the next two measures shows that this is obviously an oversight.

M. 42 (p. 5): In the MS this measure is followed by a page with three blank measures (staff lines without notation), then this measure:

(The composer arranged the instruments in the order shown, which was usual in the scores of his early and middle periods. Two errors in the rhythm of the flute part have been tacitly corrected.) This is followed in the MS by a repetition of mm. 41 & 42 with the tempo indication "Allegro molto e vivace," and these lead into m. 43. The passage is obviously still unfinished in this form. Presumably the composer made the final adjustments in the engraving copy that is now lost.

Mm. 68 & 69 (p. 8): In the first-edition parts and the MS, the horns are tied. There are a few reasons for defending the omission of the ties in the later publications and in the present edition.

M. 72 (p. 8): The first-edition parts show ties to the next measure for the two horns; these are lacking in the MS. The present edition again adopts the reading of the later publications, which omit the ties.

Mm. 74 & 75 (p. 9): Same comment as for mm. 72 & 73.

Mm. 91–99 (pp. 10 & 11): In the MS the horns and trumpets have

The following information is necessary to evaluate this: Blank measures in Beethoven's MSS usually signify full-measure rests. But when the

composer has indicated something like "unisono" or "coi corni," this remark holds until it is countermanded by new notation (actual notes). Therefore, in this case, strictly speaking, the trumpets would play along with the horns the whole time. On the other hand, in the first-edition parts the passage reads:

It is not clear why the brass should rest in mm. 93 & 94, as both sources indicate. Thus the reading of the later publications, including the present edition, which gives the horns in mm. 93 & 94 repetitions of m. 92, is probably to be defended. Of course, it is a separate question whether the composer did not wish the trumpets to follow the horns another three measures or even more. Possibly the passage was intended to read:

The present edition adopts the more recent reading:

But this is by no means certainly correct, and the composer may have intended reading (c). Since there is surely an error, or even two, in the writing and engraving of this passage, only (c) or (d) can be seriously considered. The choice must be left to the judgment of the conductor.

M. 119 (p. 12): It is probably idle to dispute whether in both violin parts the second quarter-beat should read [music] or [music] Beethoven himself wrote the semitone step

for the 1st violins (for the 2nd, he wrote "8va") and expressly canceled it with a ♮♭ on the last quarter-beat of the next measure; this is also the reading in the first-edition parts. On the other hand, in the parallel passage, m. 393, both the MS and the first-edition parts show the whole-tone step [music] for the instruments that are playing the melody. Surely the composer did not make a conscious distinction between the two passages. Therefore, it must be left to the discretion of the conductor whether he is to be literal and play the passages according to the sources, or whether he is to make them correspond one way or the other.

M. 128 (p. 13): A case similar to the preceding. The MS and the first-edition parts have no sharp before the *f* in any of the voices (the 2nd violins have "in 8va"). On the other hand, Beethoven marked the corresponding note in the later passage—transposed to the upper fourth (m. 402, p. 37)—as a leading tone. Since the two passages diverge only in a single note, this is obviously a slip of the pen on the composer's part. The reading with the more decided leading tone is to be preferred, and thus the first passage will have an *f*-sharp rather than an *f*. Probably all the newer publications accept this reading, and the present edition concurs.

M. 161 (p. 15): In the MS, the fourth quarter-beat in the oboes reads: [music]

whereas in the first-edition parts they have

On the same beat, the MS gives the 2nd violins

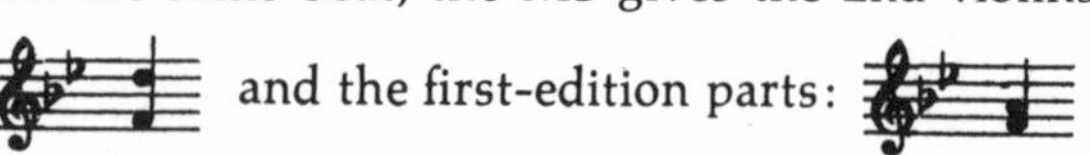

M. 183 (p. 17): The MS and all editions, including the first, give the cellos and basses the note [music]

A comparison with the parallel passage four measures earlier, and especially with the corresponding passage in the recapitulation (p. 41), shows that this is an error that has been perpetuated from the original MS to the present.

Both instruments should have a full rest. The discovery of the error is due to the careful observation of Dr. Volkmar Andreaes in Zurich.

M. 290 (p. 28): In the MS and the first-edition parts, the third quarter-beat in the 1st violins is a *b*-sharp:

The present edition has adopted the usual reading

but the passage is very dubious.

Mm. 343 & 344 (p. 31): In the MS, obviously by mistake, these notes of the 1st bassoon are lacking:

M. 487 (p. 46): For the last quarter-beat in the 1st violins, the first-edition parts have

whereas the MS has

Perhaps Beethoven made the change to the normal printed reading in the engraving copy.

M. 493 (p. 47): There is a special story attached to the sixth measure before the close of the first movement, as it has probably always been printed up to now: About the middle of the nineteenth century, it was repeatedly declared superfluous and for that reason many conductors are said to omit it even today. Robert Schumann, in two articles in the *Neue Zeitschrift für Musik* for 1840, was the first to speak of its presumed supernumerary nature. The most important of these statements, included in the review of the Gewandhaus concert of October 11, reads: "Once again after the symphony of a master of the art our attention was directed to the end of the first movement; there is obviously *one measure too many* here! Compare the score, p. 64, mm. 2, 3, 4. In view of the complete similarity in all the voices, a mistake on the part of the copyist, or even of the composer, was very easy to make. Also, after Beethoven completed a work he did not care much about following up on it. Whoever owns the original score should be good enough to look this up; naturally that is the most important source."

Not less significant is a communication found in a letter of Beethoven's pupil Carl Czerny about several doubtful passages in the master's symphonies. F. Luib published it in the April 14 issue of the second year of the *Neue Wiener Musikzeitung* (1853). This letter reads in part:

"Since I was almost always present at the performances conducted by Beethoven himself from the beginning of this century on, and sometimes had attended the preliminary rehearsals as well, and since I still possess a pretty good memory in musical matters, I believe I am correct in the following statements:

"I. At the end of the first movement of the Fourth Symphony (in B-flat, score published by Simrock in Bonn) the fourth measure (p. 64) should be deleted. The 1st violin part should read:

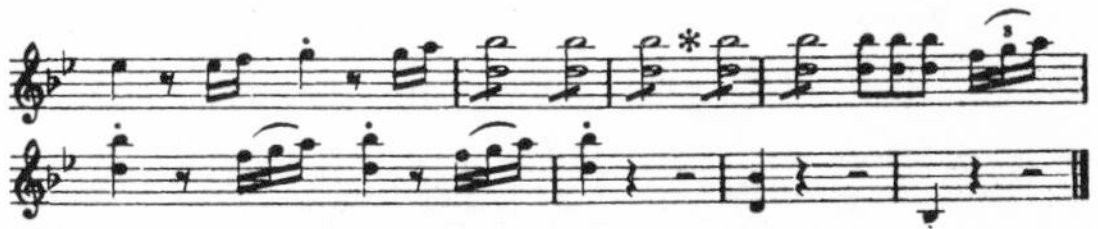

And the same in all the parts. The measure marked with the asterisk is erroneously repeated in every score. Since Beethoven's scores were often quite illegible, such oversights are explicable. . . ."

When I brought this letter to light again in an article in Hesse's *Deutscher Musikerkalender*, 1914, "On Some Unfamiliar Engraving Errors Handed Down in Beethoven's Symphonies," I thought Czerny was to be believed implicitly. After comparing the MS and the first-edition parts, however, I incline toward the view that, despite Czerny's firm assertion, Simrock's score gives the right reading of the passage in question. Both sources include the so-called superfluous measure, and it is all but impossible that the composer deleted it in the MS copy prepared for the engraver, which is apparently lost, for otherwise it would be so indicated in the first-edition parts. At most one might suppose that he omitted the measure at his concerts. This does not seem to have been the case, for in the orchestral parts corrected by Beethoven himself, now in the Archive of the Gesellschaft der Musikfreunde in Vienna, the measure is not deleted. To be sure, it is odd to find Czerny defending his cause so decidedly, but he must have been wrong all the same. A decision on the basis of metrical feeling alone is generally insufficient, especially in the case of the endings of long movements.

Second Movement

M. 1 (p. 48): The MS, by mistake, omits the cello note

M. 41 (p. 58): The MS gives the trumpets

the first-edition parts:

Since it can be assumed that Beethoven wrote the reading of the first edition into the engraving copy, that is the reading adopted here.

M. 90 (p. 69): In the MS and the first-edition parts, the first two eighth-beats in the violas are

A comparison with the similar passages in the other strings before and after shows that this is obviously a slip of the pen on the composer's part. The passage surely must read:

and it is probably printed that way in all the later publications.

M. 101 (p. 72): In both sources, the horns and trumpets have no tie between the second and third quarter-beats, perhaps only by mistake. Our edition follows the reading of the later scores, in which the ties are supplied.

Third Movement

In the first-edition parts the movement is labeled "Menuetto." Presumably Beethoven added this designation in the (now lost) engraving copy. Oddly, it was omitted in the later publications, but is restored in the present edition.

Mm. 87 & 88 (p. 79): The flute staff is notated:

an oversight of the composer's, since the score calls for only a single flute part.

Mm. 148 ff. (pp. 82 & 83): In the MS there are no ties between the first three 3/4-notes of this horn passage:

They are present in the first-edition parts. Later publications follow the MS. A comparison with the preceding measures shows that the ties are to be defended, and it can be assumed that the composer added them in the engraving copy.

Mm. 153 ff. (p. 83): In the MS and the first edition, the phrasing in the eighth-notes of the strings is handled very carelessly. Our edition strives for the greatest possible uniformity in the phrasing indications.

Fourth Movement

M. 4 (p. 90): In the MS and the first edition, the violas do not have

but instead:

The composer had apparently written the same notes an octave lower for the cellos and basses, but then corrected them vigorously to read:

and for greater clarity wrote below them the letters "h [= b] c d h." (The indication of *b*-natural instead of *b*-flat was not an error by Beethoven, as is stated in Grove-Hehemann, *Beethoven and His Nine Symphonies*, p. 122, but his usual mode of expression when the lowering or raising of a note was self-evident.) The parallel passage (m. 192, p. 109) shows clearly that we are dealing here with an error in the viola part that found its way from the MS into the first-edition parts.

M. 14 (p. 90): The MS gives the 2nd violins

whereas the first-edition parts have

A comparison with the parallel passage four measures later shows that this is clearly a printing error. The incorrect reading has also found its way into later publications, including the complete works edition.

Mm. 20–23 (p. 91): The first-edition parts give the clarinets four measures rest. In the MS the passage is unclear: in the first of these measures four notes are deleted and both "Solo" and "tutti" are indicated. Obviously the composer forgot to write out the passage and the copyist thought that, as usual in Beethoven's MSS, blank measures were to be considered as rests. The reading given in the later publications —both clarinets in unison with the 2nd oboe—

is probably correct, and is adopted in the present edition.

Mm. 34 & 35 (p. 93): The MS gives the clarinets

A comparison with the other high woodwinds shows that the reading in the first-edition parts,

which is followed by the later publications as well, is correct.

M. 188 (p. 109): In the MS and the first edition, the second quarter-beat in the 2nd violins is

The present edition follows the reading of the later publications, which have

But the passage is somewhat doubtful.

M. 257 (p. 115): In the MS, the 1st oboe part has the notes

In the first edition, these are given to the flute. This was obviously a slip of the pen on Beethoven's part, since in the parallel passage (pp. 96 & 97), too, the only woodwind playing is the flute. Presumably Beethoven corrected the error in the engraving copy. Nevertheless it is still found in the complete works edition.

Mm. 292 & 293 (p. 118): The first edition shows a rest on the first quarter-beat of the 2nd violins, thus erroneously anticipating the immediately following measure. The MS has the correct reading:

which could also be accurately supplied by comparison with the two measures immediately preceding.

Mm. 302 & 303 (p. 119): The MS and the first-edition parts generally have ties between the notes of the same pitch. In contrast to other later publications of the symphony, including the complete works edition, the present edition includes the ties as something clearly intended by Beethoven.

M. 312 (p. 121): The MS gives the 1st bassoon

whereas the first edition has

The passage is dubious. Our edition adopts the reading of the MS. In the same measure and the next two, the first edition and the MS have partial staccato indications for the bassoons, cellos and basses. This should be emphasized, because even the complete works edition does not adopt this indication. The entire passage should thus read:

Zurich February 1938

DR. MAX UNGER

Symphony No. 5 in C Minor, Op. 67

Immediately upon completion of the *Eroica* (1803) Beethoven started work on a new symphony in C minor,[1] which occupied him for some time but was set aside in favor of the far more charming and less upsetting B-flat major symphony published as the Fourth, Op. 60, in 1806. When that one was finished, Beethoven must have resumed work on the C minor right away. It must have been commissioned by Count Franz von Oppersdorff and completed by February 1808 at the latest. This is clear from an unfortunately undated letter to the Count which must be assigned to March 1808 because of the finger ailment of which Beethoven complains in the letter (Thayer-Deiters-Riemann, II, p. 11): "I will . . . only inform you that your symphony has long been ready, and I am sending it to you by the next mail—you can reserve 50 gulden for me, since the copy I had made for you comes to 50 gulden at the least. —In case you do not want the symphony, let me know before the next mailing day—but in case you take it, then delight me as soon as possible with the 300 gulden still due to me. —The last movement has 3 trombones and a piccolo—to be sure, this is not 3 drums, but will make more noise than 6 drums, and better noise."

It is clear that this can only refer to the symphony in C minor because of the indication of the finale orchestration. But even though Count Oppersdorff had paid the prearranged fee for this symphony, he still did not receive it, but got as compensation the B-flat major, Op. 60, which was printed with a dedication to him. Beethoven wrote him on November 1, 1808: "Dearest Count, You will regard me in a false light, but necessity compelled me to sell the symphony written for you and another one besides [the "Pastoral"] to someone else—but be assured that you will soon receive the one intended for you."

Only the C minor symphony and the "Pastoral" can be meant in Beethoven's letter of June 8, 1808, in which he offered the Leipzig publishing firm Breitkopf & Härtel[2] two symphonies among other works, remarking: "For several reasons I must attach the stipulation to the two symphonies that they should not be published before six months beginning June 1. —I may very well take a trip toward winter and would thus prefer that they do not yet

---

[1] When Beethoven's brother Karl wrote to Breitkopf & Härtel on October 14, 1803 (Appendix III to Thayer-Deiters, II, 2nd ed.), "You can have one or two symphonies," the first must refer to the *Eroica*, the second only to the C minor. In his letter of December 23, 1803, too, Karl van Beethoven still speaks of two symphonies, but on October 10, 1804, only one (the *Eroica*), which proves that the other one was not yet completed. Sketches for the first two movements and for a later abandoned 6/8 finale, which occur alongside drafts for the piano concerto in G, Op. 58, and the F major trio "Gut, Söhnchen, gut" of *Leonore*, are printed by Gustav Nottebohm in his 1872 *Beethoveniana*, pp. 10 ff. Nottebohm remarks: "The main motif of the first movement of the C minor symphony, consisting of four notes, is also contained in its rhythmic form in the main theme of the piano concerto in G major." Other 1805 sketches for the second and third movements of the symphony, which was thereby nearing completion, occur along with the beginning of the overture posthumously published as Op. 138 (*Leonore* No. 1?) and the just begun sonata for piano and cello Op. 69; Nottebohm printed these, *op. cit.*, pp. 62 ff. Other sketches, including some on separate sheets for the third movement and the transition to the fourth, and some for the first movement in company with the first movement and main theme of the rondo finale of the violin concerto (completed 1806) and the sonata Op. 69, are published in Nottebohm's *Zweite Beethoveniana*, pp. 528 ff.

[2] Cf. Oskar von Hase, *Breitkopf & Härtel, Gedenkschrift*, 4th ed., vol. I, 1917, pp. 171 ff.

become known in the summer at least." With regard to the fee, Beethoven, who had at first asked 900 gulden altogether for both symphonies, the Mass in C and the sonata Op. 69, was accommodating to the publishers. On July 16, 1808, he wrote them: "I give you the Mass, the 2 symphonies, the cello and piano sonata and two additional piano sonatas,[3] or instead of these perhaps another symphony,[4] for 700 gulden. . . . You see, I am giving more and taking less—but that is the limit—you must take the Mass or I cannot give you the other works. . . . As soon as you accept my proposal, as I have no doubt you will, you will immediately receive the 2 symphonies, the cello sonata, the Mass—the two other piano sonatas or perhaps a symphony instead, in 4 weeks at most—but please let me have the fee as soon as you receive the first 4 works; I will enter the symphony or else the 2 sonatas in the contract you are to receive from me and oblige myself in writing, so you have no doubts, to send you the sonatas or the symphony." Beethoven did not conclude his agreement with the firm until September 14, 1808, when Gottfried Christoph Härtel visited him in Vienna.

Both symphonies were first performed on December 22, 1808, in the Theater an der Wien; oddly, the program calls the C minor the Sixth and the "Pastoral" the Fifth. On January 7, 1809, Beethoven wrote to the Leipzig publishers: "You would do me a very great favor, and I sincerely urge you to do this, if you do not publish all the things you have received from me until Easter; I will surely come to see you during Lent; also, do not allow any of the new symphonies to be performed before then, because, when I come to Leipzig, it will be a real treat to perform them with the Leipzig musicians, whose uprightness and good will I know so well—also I will correct the music when I arrive."

But nothing came of this trip to Leipzig, since Beethoven did not accept the position of conductor to King Jerome of Westphalia that had been offered him. On March 4, 1809, he wrote to Breitkopf & Härtel: "Both symphonies dedicated to the two gentlemen together, that is, His Excellency Count Rasumovsky and His Eminence Prince Lobkowitz—Symphony in C Minor, Op. 60 [published as 67], Symphony in F, Op. 61 [68]. Tomorrow you will receive a list of minor corrections which I made when the symphonies were performed. When I gave them to you, I had not yet heard them—and no one should try to be so godlike that he will not make improvements in his works here and there."

On March 28, 1809, he wrote further: "Here you have the piano [the correct reading of this word is probably "small"] corrections for the symphonies. Have them made directly on the plates. . . . You said you had found another error in the third movement of the C minor symphony; I don't remember what sort it was. The best thing would be to send me the proofs with the score that you receive; in a few days you will have everything back again." When a repeat of the whole Scherzo and Trio before the coda was eliminated, the two measures of the Prima Volta had been left standing in the engraving copy of the parts. The engravers must have reported this, and the publishers must have written to Beethoven about it. It is uncertain whether the publishers' reply to Beethoven's query of March 28, 1809, never arrived, or whether Beethoven merely forgot to write about this again; but, at any rate, these two measures were retained in the printed parts. Beethoven did not raise this point until some time later; in a letter of August 21, 1810, he requested that these measures be deleted. On October 15, 1810, he asked once more: "Has the change been made that I requested in the third movement? Two measures too many; I have a vague recollection that you queried me about this, but perhaps I forgot to answer you at once, and so they stayed in."

Oddly, the publishers did not have the measures deleted, so that they were even carried over into their 1825 score. The facts of the matter were discovered only in 1846, by Mendelssohn, and reported by the publishers in the *Allgemeine musikalische Zeitung* of July 8, 1846, along with a facsimile of Beethoven's letter of August 21, 1810; cf. also Nottebohm, *Beethoveniana*, 1871, pp. 17 ff.

The original MS of the score was presented by the Mendelssohn-Bartholdy family in 1908 to the Music Division of the Prussian State Library in Berlin.

The title of the parts edition published in April 1809 reads: "Sinfonie pour 2 Violons, 2

---

[3] These must be the two piano trios Op. 70.

[4] This refers to the still unprinted Fourth Symphony, Op. 60, but this was published by the Vienna Industrie-Kontor at practically the same time that the Fifth and Sixth were published in Leipzig.

Violes, Violoncelle et Contre-Violon, 2 Flûtes, petite Flûte, 2 Hautbois, 2 Clarinettes, 2 Bassons, Contre-Basson, 2 Cors, 2 Trompettes, Timbales et 3 Trompes. Composée et dediée à son Altesse Sérénissime Monseigneur le Prince régnant de Lobkowitz, duc de Raudnitz et à son Excellence Monsieur le Comte de Rasumoffsky par Louis van Beethoven. Propriété des Editeurs (OEuv. 67) No 5 des Sinfonies; à Leipsic chez Breitkopf & Härtel" (publication number 1329).

The publishers did not bring out the score until the end of 1825.[5]

Beethoven did not add the metronome marks till later, at the same time as those for Symphonies 1 through 4 and 6 through 8; all these were published in the supplement to the *Allgemeine musikalische Zeitung*, Leipzig, of December 17, 1817.

Berlin WILHELM ALTMANN

[5] Cf. the news sheet of the *Allgemeine musikalische Zeitung* of January 1826.

Ludwig van Beethoven

FOURTH AND FIFTH SYMPHONIES

in Full Orchestral Score

Symphony No. 4

I

L. van Beethoven, Op. 60
1770 - 1827

10
Fl.
Ob.
Cl.
Fg.
Cor. (B)
Vl.
Vla.
Vc. Cb
sempre pp
1.
pizz.
zu 2
fp dim.
pp
fp
f
arco
Vc.
Cb.

20
Fl.
Ob.
Cl.
Fg.
Vl.
Vla.
Vc.
Cb.
1.
pp
pizz.
30
Cor.
(B)
fp
sfp
arco
f
p
Vc.
Cb.

Fl.
Cl.
Fg.
Vl.
Vla.
Vc.
Cb.
1.
dim.
pp
cresc.
arco
Allegro vivace o = 80
Fl.
Ob.
Cl.
Fg.
Cor. (B)
Tr. (B)
Timp.
Vl.
Vla.
Vc. Cb.
ff
ff sempre
tr

40

Fl.

Ob.

Cl

Fg.

Cor. (B)

Tr. (B)

Timp.

Vl.

fp

Vla.

fp

Vc.

fp

Cb.

50

Ob.

1.

p dolce

Cl.

p dolce

Fg.

p dolce

Cor. (B)

p

Vl.

Vla.

Vc.

Fl.
ff
ff sempre
Ob.
ff
zu 2
ff sempre
Cl.
ff
zu 2
ff sempre
Fg.
zu 2
ff
ff sempre
Cor. (B)
ff
ff sempre
Tr. (B)
ff
ff sempre
Timp.
ff
ff sempre
Vl.
ff
3
ff sempre
ff
3
ff sempre
Vla.
ff
ff sempre
Vc. Cb.
ff
ff sempre

60
Fl.
Ob.
Cl.
Fg.
Cor. (B)
Tr. (B)
Timp.
Vl.
Vla.
Vc. Cb.
sf

Fl.
Ob.
1.
pp
Cl
pp
1.
Fg.
zu 2
pp
Cor.
(B)
pp
Tr.
(B)
Timp.
Vl.
pp
Vla.
pp
pizz.
Vc.
Cb.
pp
70
Ob.
Cl.
Fg.
Cor.
(B)
Vl.
pp
Vla.
Vc.
Cb.

Fl.
Ob.
Cl.
Fg.
Cor. (B)
Vl.
Vla.
Vc. Cb.
p
1.
cresc.
arco
80
Fl.
Ob.
Cl.
Fg.
Cor. (B)
Tr. (B)
Timp.
Vl.
Vla.
Vc. Cb.
cresc.
ff
sf
f
5

Fl.
Ob.
Cl.
Fg.
Cor.
(B)
Tr.
(B)
Timp.
Vl.
Vla.
Vc.
Cb.
90
zu 2

Fl.
Ob.
Cl.
Fg.
Cor. (B)
Tr. (B)
Vl.
Vla.
Vc. Cb.
zu 2
sf
100
Vc.
Cb.
sf dim.
dim.

110
Fl.
Ob.
Fg.
1.
p
sempre p
Vl.
Vla.
Bassi
Vc.
Cb.
120
#?

130
Fg.
Vl.
Vla.
Vc.
Cb.
pp
cresc.
Fl.
Ob.
Cl.
Fg.
Cor.
(B)
Tr.
(B)
Timp.
Vl.
Vla.
Vc.
Cb.
f
tr

140
Fl.
Ob.
Cl.
Fg.
Cor (B)
Tr. (B)
Pk.
Vl.
Vla.
Vc. Cb.
1.
p dolce
tr
150

Fl.
Ob.
Cl.
Fg.
Vl.
Vla.
Vc.
Cb.
1.
p
160
ff
Cor.
(B)
Tr.
(B)
Timp.
pp
pp cresc.

170
Fl.
Ob.
Cl.
zu 2
cresc.
Fg.
zu 2
cresc.
Cor. (B)
zu 2
Tr. (B)
zu 2
Timp.
tr
Vl.
Vla.
Vc.
Cb.
f
ff

180

Fl.
Ob.
Cl.
Fg.
Cor. (B)
Tr. (B)
Timp.
Vl.
Vla.
Vc. Cb.

f

sempre f

sempre f

sempre f

sempre f

1.

Fl.
Ob.
Cl.
Fg.
Cor. (B)
Tr. (B)
Timp.
Vl.
Vla.
Vc. Cb.

1.
Fl.
Ob.
Cl.
Fg.
Cor. (B)
Tr. (B)
Timp.
Vl.
Vla
Vc. Cb.
ff
tr
5

2.
Fl.
Ob.
Cl.
Fg.
Cor. (B)
Tr. (B)
Timp
Vl.
Vla.
Vc.
Cb.
fp
fp
fp
fp
3
3
3

190
Fl.
Ob.
Cl
Fg.
Cor.
(B)
Tr.
(B)
Timp.
Vl.
Vla.
Vc.
Cb.
sempre f
sempre f
sempre f
sempre f
Fl.
Ob.
Cl.
Fg.
Vl.
Vla.
Vc.
Cb.

200
Fl.
Ob.
Cl.
Fg.
Vl.
Vla.
Vc.
Cb.
sf
p
p dimin.
pp

210
Vl. I.
Vc.
Fl.
cresc.
Vl.
cresc.
cresc.
Vla.
cresc.
Vc.
cresc.
220
Fl.
fp
Fg.
1.
Vl.
fp
fp
Vla.
fp
Vc.
fp
pizz.
Cb.
p
fp
p

Fl.
Cl.
Fg.
Vl.
pizz.
pizz.
Vla.
Vc.
Cb.
1.
230
Ob.
p
arco
pizz.

Fl.
Ob.
Cl.
Fg.
Vl.
Vla.
Vc.
Cb.
1.
pizz.
arco
p
cresc.
240
Cor.
(B)
Tr.
(B)
zu 2
ff

250
Fl.
Ob.
Cl.
Fg.
Cor. (B)
Tr. (B)
Vl.
Vla.
Vc. Cb.
fp
p
ff

260
Fl.
Ob.
Cl.
Fg.
Cor. (B)
Tr. (B)
Timp.
Vl.
Vla.
Vc. Cb.
ff
sempre f

270
Fl.
Ob.
Cl.
Fg.
Cor. (B)
Tr. (B)
Timp.
Vl.
Vla.
Vc. Cb.
p
pp
dim.
sempre pp
280
tr
ppp

290
Timp
Vl.
sempre pp
sempre pp
Vla.
sempre pp
Vc.
sempre pp
Cb.
300
Fl.
pp
Vl.
pp
pp
Vla.
pp
Vc.
310
Fl.
Cor. (B)
pp
tr
Timp:
pp
sempre pp
Vl.
5
Vla
Vc. Cb.
pp

tr
Timp.
Vl.
sempre pp
sempre pp
Vla.
sempre pp
Vc.
sem-
320
Timp.
Vl. I.
Vla.
Vc.
pre pp
Timp.
cresc.
Vl.
cresc.
cresc.
Vla.
cresc.
Vc.
cresc.

330
Timp.
Vl.
Vla.
Vc.
Cb.
cresc.
Fl.
Ob.
Cl.
Fg.
zu 2
Cor.
(B)
Tr.
(B)
zu 2
Timp.
Vl.
Vla.
Vc.
Cb.
ff

340
Fl.
Ob.
Cl.
Fg.
Cor (B)
Tr. (B)
Timp.
Vl.
Vla.
Vc.
Cb.
zu 2
1.
fp
p
350
dolce
cresc.
Bassi

Fl.
ff
sf
sf
sf
zu 2
Ob.
ff
sf
sf
sf
Cl.
ff
sf
sf
sf
Fg.
ff
sf
sf
sf
Cor.
(B)
ff
sf
sf
sf
Tr.
(B)
ff
Timp.
ff
Vl.
ff
sf
sf
sf
ff
Vla.
ff
Vc.
Cb.
ff

360
Fl.
Ob.
Cl.
Fg.
Cor. (B)
Tr. (B)
Timp.
Vl.
Vla.
Vc. Cb.

Fl.
Ob.
Cl.
Fg.
Cor.
(B)
Tr.
(B)
Timp.
Vl.
Vla
Vc.
Cb.
sf
ff
zu 2
tr

370
Fl.
Ob.
zu 2
Cl.
Fg.
zu 2
Cor. (B)
Tr. (B)
Timp.
Vl.
Vla.
Vc.
Cb.

380
Ob.
Cl
Fg.
Vl.
Vla.
Vc.
Cb.
1.
p
390
Fl.
Ob
Cl.
Cor. (B)
Vl.
Vla.
Vc. Cb.
sempre p
p

400
Fl.
pp cresc.
cresc.
Cor. (B)
Vl.
pp cresc.
cresc.
pp cresc.
cresc.
Vla.
p cresc.
cresc.
Vc. Cb.
pp cresc.
cresc.
410
Fl.
f
Ob.
f
Cl.
f
Fg.
zu 2
f
Cor. (B)
f
Tr. (B)
f
Timp.
f
Vl.
f
f
Vla.
f
Vc. Cb.
f

Fl.
Ob.
Cl.
Fg.
Cor. (B)
Tr. (B)
Timp
Vl.
Vla.
Vc. Cb.
tr.
zu 2
1.
p dolce
420
Timp.
Vc.
zu 2

430

Fl.
Ob.
Fg.
zu 2
2.
Cor. (B)
Tr. (B)
Timp.
Vl.
Vla.
Vc. Cb.

Fl.
Ob.
Cl.
Fg.
Cor. (B)
Tr. (B)
Timp.
Vl.
Vla.
Vc. Cb.
1.
p
pp
ff
f

440
Fl.
Ob.
Cl.
Fg.
Cor. (B)
Tr. (B)
Timp.
Vl.
Vla.
Vc.
Cb.
zu 2
zu 2
cresc.
cresc.
cresc.
pp cresc.
pp cresc.
pp cresc.
pp cresc.
f
ff
tr

450
Fl.
Ob.
Cl.
Fg.
Cor. (B)
Tr. (B)
Timp.
Vl.
Vla.
Vc. Cb.
sf
tr

460
Fl.
Ob.
Cl.
Fg.
Cor. (B)
Tr. (B)
Timp.
Vl.
Vla.
Vc. Cb.
ff
tr

470
Fl.
Ob.
Cl.
Fg.
zu 2
Cor. (B)
Tr. (B)
Timp.
Vl.
Vla.
Vc. Cb.

Fl.
Ob.
1.
p
f
Cl.
Fg.
Cor (B)
Tr. (B)
Timp.
Vl.
Vla.
Vc. Cb.

480
Fl.
Ob.
Cl.
Fg.
Cor. (B)
Tr. (B)
Timp.
Vl.
Vla.
Vc. Cb.
zu 2
zu 2
p
f
p cresc.

490
Fl.
cresc.
Ob.
cresc.
Cl.
cresc.
Fg.
cresc.
Cor.
(B)
Tr.
(B)
tr
tr
Timp.
cresc.
5
Vl.
Vla.
Vc.
Cb.

Fl.
Ob.
Cl.
Fg.
Cor. (B)
Tr. (B)
Timp.
Vl.
Vla.
Vc. Cb.
ff
tr
3

II

Adagio ♩= 84
Flauto
2 Oboi.
2 Clarinetti in B
2 Fagotti.
2 Corni in Es
2 Trombe in Es
Timpani in Es-B
Violino I.
Violino II.
Viola.
Violoncello
Contrabasso
p
cantabile
Vl.
Vla.
Vc.
cresc.
sf

Cl.
Fg.
Vl.
Vla.
Vc.
cresc.
cresc.
cresc.
cresc.
cresc.
cresc.
sempre staccato
sempre staccato
10
Fl.
Ob.
Cl.
Fg.
Cor.
(Es)
Tr.
(Es)
Timp.
Vl.
Vla.
Vc.
Cb.
p cantabile
zu 2.
zu 2
pizz.
pizz.

Fl.
Ob.
Cl.
Fg.
Cor. (Es)
Vl.
Vla.
Vc. Cb.
cresc.
sf
p
arco
1.

Fl.
Ob.
Cl.
Fg.
Cor. (Es)
Tr. (Es)
zu 2
Timp.
Vl.
Vla.
arco
Vc.
arco
Cb.

20
Fl.
fp
Ob.
f
sf
sf
sf
fp
Cl.
f
sf
sf
sf
fp
Fg.
fp
Cor.
(Es)
f
sf
sf
sf
fp
zu 2
Tr.
(Es)
f
Timp.
f
Vl.
sf
f
fp
f
sf
sf
sf
fp
Vla.
sf
sf
sf
f
fp
Vc.
f
sf
sf
sf
fp
Cb.
f
fp

Fl.
Ob.
Cl.
Fg.
Cor. (Es)
Tr. (Es)
Timp.
Vl.
Vla.
Vc.
Cb.
zu 2
1.
f
sf
fp
p

Fl.
Ob.
Fg.
Vl.
Vla.
Vc.
Cb
fp
cresc.
Cl.
f
dim.
pp
p cantabile
legato

Cl.
legato
Vl.
pizz.
Vla.
Vc.
Cb.
30
Cl.
cresc.
p
Fg.
cresc.
Vl.
cresc.
p
cresc.
p
pizz.
Vla.
cresc.
p
pizz.
Vc.
Cb.
Bassi
p

Fl.
Ob.
Cl.
Fg.
Cor. (Es)
Vl.
Vla.
Vc.
Cb.
cresc.
zu 2
arco
dolce
f
p

Fl.
Ob.
Cl.
Fg.
Cor. (Es)
Vl.
Vc. Cb.
p dolce
p dolce
p dolce
zu 2
p dolce
Fl.
Ob.
Cl.
Fg.
Cor. (Es)
Vl.
Vla.
Vc. Cb.
cresc.
sempre cresc.
zu 2
cresc.
sempre cresc.
cresc.
zu 2
sempre cresc.
cresc.
zu 2
sempre cresc.
cresc.
sempre cresc.
cresc.
sempre cresc.
cresc.
sempre cresc.
cresc.
sempre cresc.
cresc.
sempre cresc.

40
Fl.
Ob.
Cl.
Fg.
Cor.
(Es)
Tr.
(Es)
Timp.
Vl.
Vla.
Vc.
Cb.
ff
zu 2
p cantabile
p
cresc.
sf

Cl.
Fg.
Vl.
Vla.
Vc.
cresc.
p
Fl.
Ob.
Cl.
Fg.
Cor. (Es)
Tr. (Es)
Timp.
Vl.
Vla.
Vc.
Cb.
zu 2
50
f
ff
sf

Fl.
f sempre
Ob.
f sempre
Cl.
Fg.
Cor. (Es)
f sempre
Tr. (Es)
Timp.
Vl.
Vla.
Vc.
Cb.

Fl.
Ob.
Cl.
Fg.
Cor. (Es)
Tr. (Es)
Timp.
Vl.
Vla.
Vc.
Cb.
Vl.
zu 2
sf
p
p espressivo
espressivo

1.
Fg.
Vl.
Vla.
Vc.
60
1.
Cl.
Fg.
Vl.
Vla.
Bassi
Vc.
Fl.
pp cantabile
Cl.
Fg.
Cor
(Es)
Timp.
Vl.
Vla.
pizz.
Vc.
Cb.
pizz.

Fl.
Ob.
Cl.
Fg.
Cor.
(Es)
Vl.
Vla.
Vc.
Cb.
p
cresc.
sf
1.
arco

70
Fl.
cresc.
Ob.
cresc.
1.
Cl.
cresc.
Fg.
cresc.
Cor.
(Es)
cresc.
Tr.
(Es)
p cresc.
Timp.
p cresc.
Vl.
cresc.
cresc.
Vla.
cresc.
Vc.
Cb.
cresc.

Fl.
Ob.
Cl.
Fg.
Cor. (Es)
Tr. (Es)
Timp.
Vl.
Vla.
Vc.
Cb.
arco
arco

Fl.
Ob.
Cl.
Fg.
Cor.
(Es)
Tr.
(Es)
Timp.
Vl.
Vla.
Vc.
Cb.

Fl.
Ob.
Cl.
Fg.
Cor. (Es)
zu 2
Vl.
Vla.
Vc.
Cb.
f
sf
fp
p
Ob.
Cl.
Fg.
Cor. (Es)
Vl.
Vla.
Vc. Cb.
fp
cresc.

80
Ob.
Cl.
Cor. (Es)
Vl.
Vla.
Vc.
Cb.
f
dimin.
pp
1.
p cantabile
legato
pp legato
cresc.
pizz.

Fl.
Ob.
Cl.
Fg.
Cor. (Es)
Vl.
Vla.
Vc. Cb.
p
cresc.
zu 2
arco
f
90
dolce
Vc.
Cb.

Fl.
Ob.
Cl.
Fg.
Cor. (Es)
Vl.
Vc. Cb.
dolce
dolce
dolce
dolce
Fl.
Ob.
Cl.
Fg.
Vl.
Vla.
Vc. Cb.
sempre
perdendo
sempre
perdendo
sempre
perdendo
sempre
perdendo
sempre
perdendo
sempre
perdendo
perdendo
sempre
perdendo

Fl.
pp
3

Ob.

Cl.
1.
pp
3
pp

Fg.
pp

Cor. (Es)
2.
pp

Vl.
pizz.
pp
arco
pizz.
pp

Vla.
pizz.
pp

Vc.
perdendo
pp

Cb.
pizz.
pp

100

Fl.
pp

Ob.
1.
cresc.

Cl.
1.
cresc.

Fg.
1.
cresc.

Cor. (Es)
cresc.

Vl.
pp
cresc.
arco
cresc.

Vla.
p cresc.

Vc.
p cresc.

Cb.
arco
p cresc.

Fl.
Ob.
Cl.
Fg.
Cor. (Es)
Tr. (Es)
Timp.
Vl.
Vla.
Vc.
Cb.
ff
pp
cresc.
tr
pizz.
arco
8

III

Menuetto. Allegro vivace 𝅗𝅥. = 100

Fl.
Ob.
Cl.
Fg.
Cor. (B)
Tr. (B)
Timp.
Vl.
Vla.
Vc. Cb
cresc
f
ff
sf
Fl.
Ob.
Vl.
Vla.
Vc.
p

30
Fl.
Ob.
Fg.
Vl.
Vla.
Vc.
sempre
zu 2
40
p
sempre p

Fl.
Ob.
Cl.
Fg.
cresc.
Vl.
cresc.
cresc.
Vla.
cresc.
Vc.
cresc.
50
Fl.
f
ff
Ob.
f
ff
Cl.
1.
f
ff
p
Fg.
1.
f
ff
p
Cor.
(B)
f
ff
Tr.
(B)
f
ff
Timp.
f
ff
Vl.
f
ff
f
ff
Vla.
f
ff
Vc.
Cb.
Vc.
Bassi
f
ff

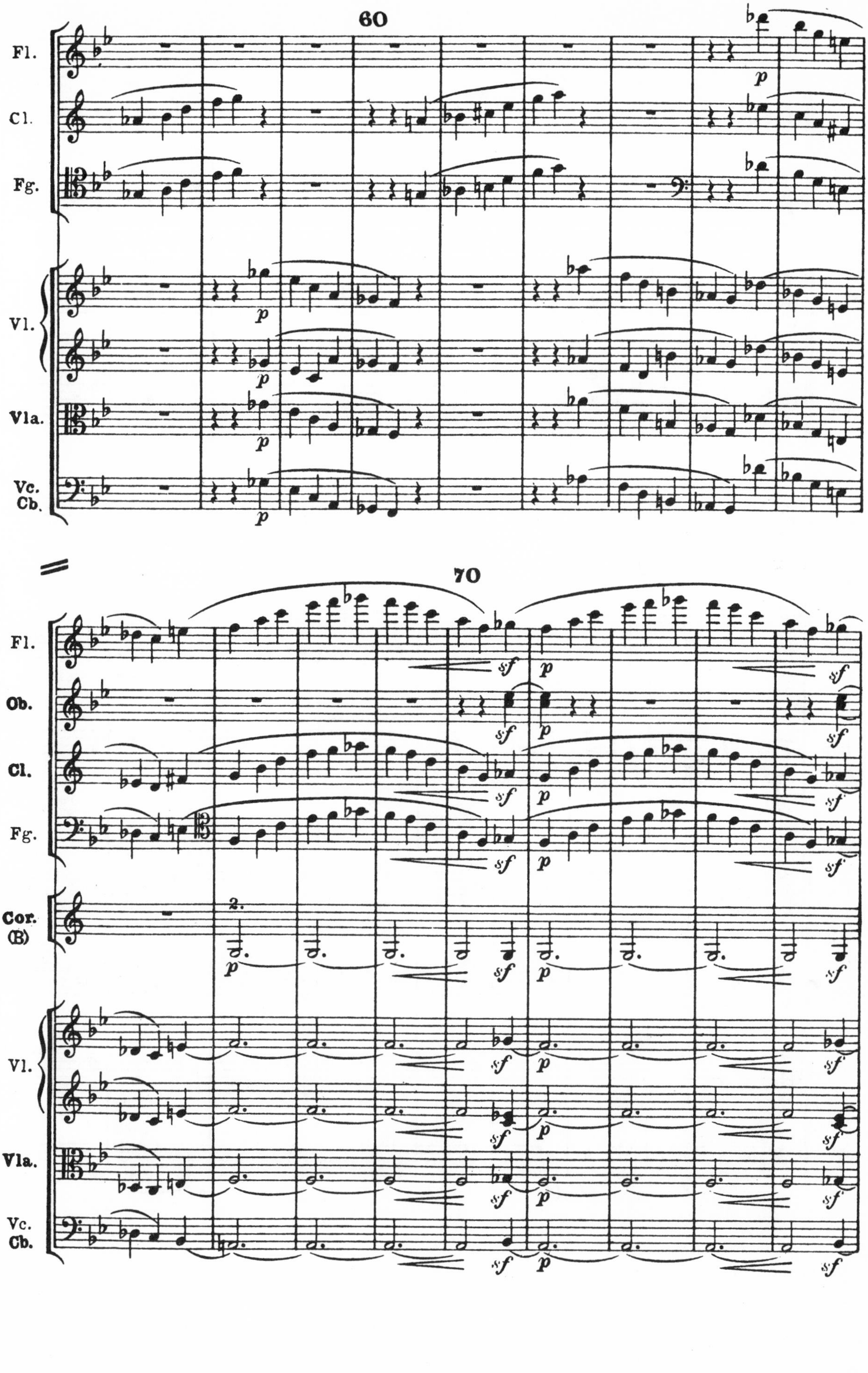

60

Fl.
Cl.
Fg.
Vl.
Vla.
Vc.
Cb.

70

Fl.
Ob.
Cl.
Fg.
Cor. (B)
Vl.
Vla.
Vc.
Cb.

80
Fl.
Ob.
Cl.
zu 2
Fg.
zu 2
Cor. (B)
Tr. (B)
Timp.
tr
Vl.
Vla.
Vc. Cb.
f
ff

90
Fl.
Ob.
Cl.
Fg.
Cor (B)
Tr. (B)
Timp.
Vl.
Vla.
Vc. Cb.
f
tr

Trio

Un poco meno Allegro 𝅗𝅥. = 88

120
Fl.
Ob.
Cl.
Fg.
Cor.
(B)
zu 2
130
pizz.
Vl.
sul G
arco
Vla.
Vc.
Cb.
Vla
Vc.

140

Fl.
pp
cresc. poco a poco

Ob.
pp
cresc. poco a poco

Cl.
pp
cresc. poco a poco

Fg.
pp
cresc. poco a poco

Cor. (B)
pp
cresc. poco a poco

Vl.
cresc. poco a poco
sf
cresc. poco a poco

Vla.
cresc. poco a poco

Vc.
cresc. poco a poco

150

Fl.

Ob.

Cl.

Fg.

Cor. (B)

Vl.
sf

Vla.

Vc.

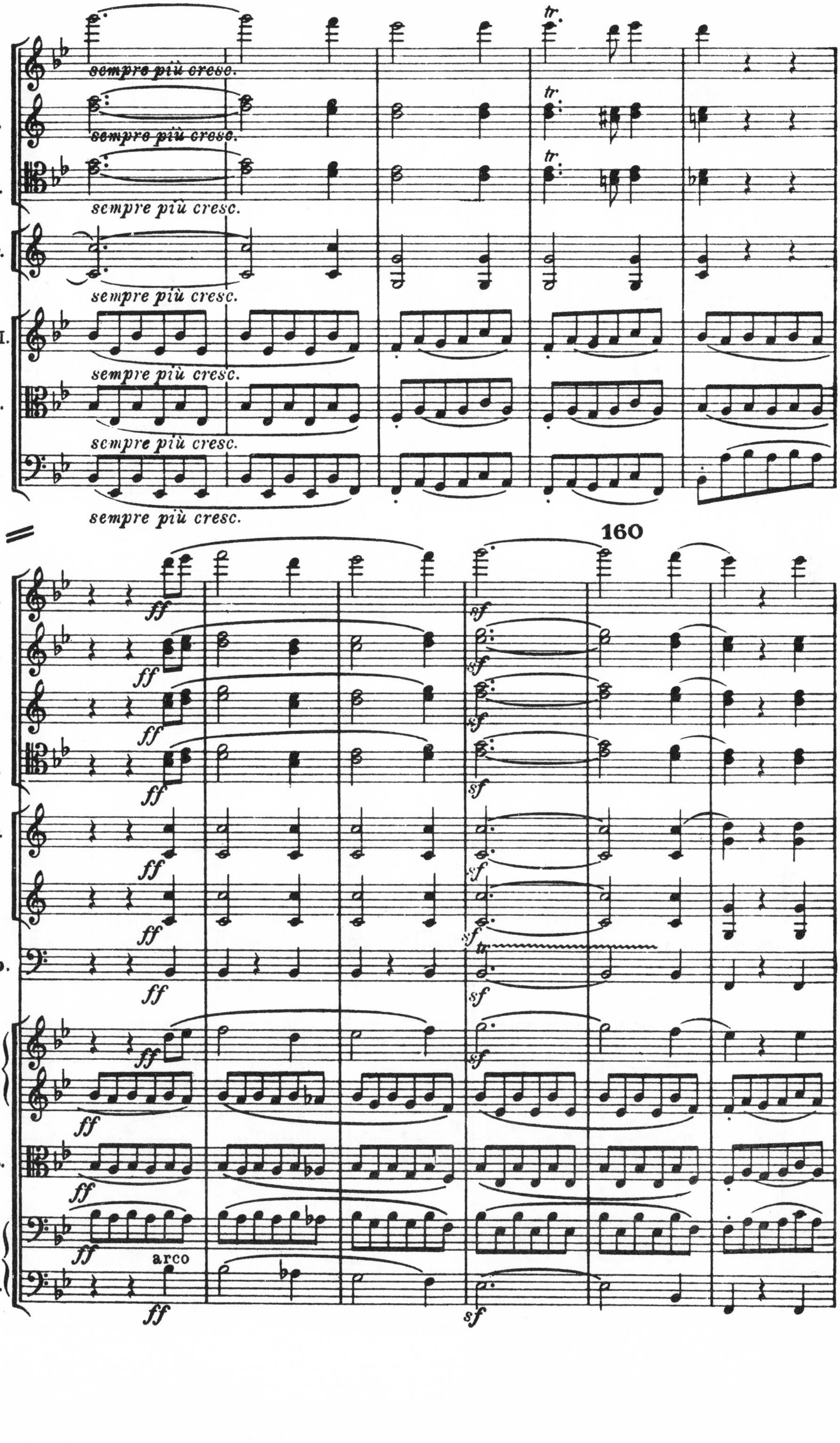
Fl.
Cl.
Fg.
Cor. (B)
Vl.II.
Vla.
Vc.
sempre più cresc.
tr.
160
Fl.
Ob.
Cl.
Fg.
Cor. (B)
Tr. (B)
Timp.
Vl.
Vla.
Vc.
Cb.
ff
sf
arco

tr.
Fl.
Ob.
Cl.
Fg.
Cor.
(B)
Tr.
(B)
Timp.
Vl.
Vla.
Vc.
Cb.
sf
dim.

170
Fl.
Ob.
Cl.
Fg.
Cor (B)
Tr. (B)
Timp.
Vl.
Vla.
Vc.
Cb.
dimin.
pp

Tempo I 𝅗𝅥. = 100
Fl.
Ob.
Cl.
Fg.
Cor. (B)
Tr. (B)
Timp.
Vl.
Vla.
Vc.
Cb.
f
ff
cresc.
Alla repetizione dal 𝄋 al 𝄌
Scherzo da capo dal 𝄋 Pag. 73.

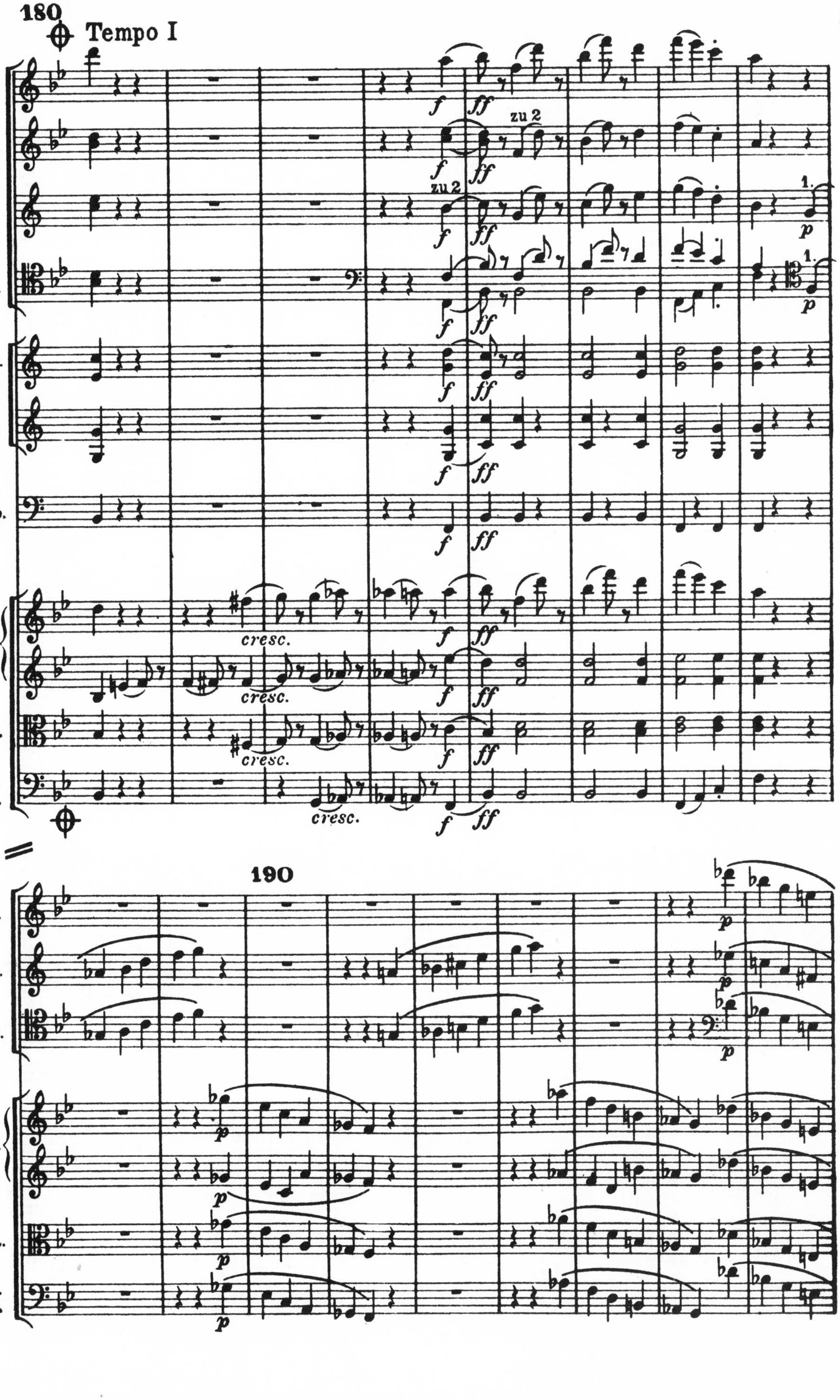

180

Tempo I

Fl.

Ob.

Cl.

Fg.

Cor. (B)

Tr. (B)

Timp.

Vl.

Vla.

Vc. Cb.

f *ff* zu 2 zu 2 1. *p* *cresc.*

190

Fl.

Cl.

Fg.

Vl.

Vla.

Vc. Cb.

p

200
Fl.
Ob.
Cl.
Fg.
Cor. (B)
Vl.
Vla.
Vc. Cb.
210
Fl.
Ob.
Cl.
Fg.
Cor. (B)
Tr. (B)
Timp.
Vl.
Vla.
Vc. Cb.
zu 2
sf
p
f
ff
tr

220
Fl.
Ob.
Cl.
Fg.
Cor. (B)
Tr. (B)
Timp.
Vl.
Vla.
Vc. Cb.
f
ff
p
cresc.

IV

Allegro ma non troppo 𝅗𝅥=80
Flauto
2 Oboi
2 Clarinetti in B
2 Fagotti
2 Corni in B
2 Trombe in B
Timpani in B-F
Violino I
Violino II
Viola
Violoncello e Contrabasso
Vl.
Vc. Cb.
10
Vla.

Fl.
Cl.
Fg.
Vl.
Vla.
Vc.
Cb.
20
Fl.
Ob.
Cl.
Fg.
Cor.
(B)
Tr.
(B)
Timp
Vl.
Vla.
Vc.
Cb.
zu 2
zu 2
cresc.
ff
p

30
Fl.
Ob.
Cl.
zu 2
Fg.
zu 2
Cor. (B)
Tr. (B)
Timp.
Vl.
Vla.
Vc. Cb.

Fl.
Ob.
Cl.
Fg.
Cor. (B)
Tr. (B)
Vl.
Vla.
Vc. Cb
zu 2
zu 2
dimin.
1.
p dolce
1.
p 3 3
dimin.
p
p
p
p
40
p

Vl.
Vla.
Vc.
Cb.
50
Fl.
Ob.
Cl.
Fg.
Cor.
(B)
Tr.
(B)
zu 2
1.
f
p

60
Fl.
Ob.
Cl.
Fg.
Cor (B)
Tr. (B)
Vl.
Vla.
Vc. Cb.
zu 2
f
Timp.
ff
sf

70
Vl.
Vla
Vc.
Fl.
Ob.
Cl.
Fg.
Cor.
(B)
Tr.
(B)
Timp.
Vl.
Vla.
Vc.
Cb.

80

Fl.

Ob.

Fg.

Vl.

Vla.

Vc.

cresc.

p *cresc.*

Fl.

Ob.

Cl.

Fg.

Cor. (B)

Tr. (B)

Timp

Vl.

Vla.

Vc.

Cb.

ff

tr

90
Fl.
1.
Ob.
1.
Fg.
Cor.
(B)
Tr.
(B)
Timp.
tr
Vl.
Vla.
Vc.
Cb.

Fl.
Ob.
Cl.
Fg.
Cor. (B)
Tr. (B)
Timp.
Vl.
Vla.
Vc.
Cb.

100
1.
2.
Fl.
Ob.
Cl.
Fg.
Cor.
(B)
Tr.
(B)
Timp.
Vl.
Vla.
Vc.
Cb.
Vl.
Vla.
Vc.
Cb.

110
Vl.
cresc.
cresc.
Vla.
cresc.
Vc.
cresc.
Vl.
f
f
Vla.
f
Vc.
f
120
Fl.
ff
Ob.
ff
Fg.
ff
Vl.
più f
ff
p
più f
ff
p
Vla.
più f
ff
p
Vc.
più f
ff
p
Cb.
ff
p

Fl.
Cl.
Fg.
Vl.
Vla.
Vc.
Cb.
1.
p
130
Ob.
Fg.
Cor
(B)
Vl.
Vla.
Vc.
Cb.
cresc.
f
sfp

Ob.
Cl.
Fg.
Vl.
Vla.
Vc.
Cb.
1.
p
f
sfp
140
1.
p
f

1.
Ob.
1.
Cl.
1.
Fg.
Vl.
sf
p
sf
p
Vla.
sf
p
Vc.
Cb.
sf
p
150
1.
Ob.
pp
pp
zu 2
Cl.
pp
pp
Fg.
pp
Vl.
pp
pp
Vla.
pp
Vc.
pp

Fl.
Ob.
Cl.
Fg.
Vl.
Vla.
Vc.

zu 2

cresc.

160

Fl.
Ob.
Cl.
Fg.
Cor. (B)
Tr. (B)
Timp.
Vl.
Vla.
Vc. Cb.

ff

170
Fl.
Ob.
Cl.
Fg.
Cor. (B)
Tr. (B)
Timp.
Vl.
Vla.
Vc.
Cb.
sf

Fl.
Ob.
Cl.
Fg.
Cor. (B)
Tr. (B)
Timp.
Vl.
Vla.
Vc.
Cb.
sf

180
Fl.
Ob.
Cl.
Fg.
Cor. (B)
Tr. (B)
Timp.
Vl.
Vla.
Vc.
Cb.
sf
1.
p dolce
dim.
p

Fg.
zu 2
p
Vl.
pizz.
pizz.
p
Vla.
pizz.
p
Vc.
pizz.
arco
p
190
Fl.
f
Ob.
f
Cl.
f
Fg.
f
Cor. (B)
f
Tr. (B)
f
Timp.
f
Vl.
arco
f
arco
f
Vla.
arco
f
Vc. Cb.
f

200
Fl.
Ob.
Cl.
Fg.
Cor. (B)
Tr. (B)
Timp.
Vl.
Vla.
Vc. Cb.
zu 2
1.
p

210

Fl. *f* *ff*

Ob. zu 2 *f* *ff*

Cl. zu 2 *f* *ff* *dim.*

Fg. zu 2 *f* *ff*

Cor. (B) *ff*

Tr. (B) *ff*

Timp. *ff*

Vl. *f* *ff* *dim.*

f *ff*

Vla. *f* *ff*

Vc. Cb. *f* *ff*

1. 220

Ob. *p*

Cl. *dolce* *p* 3 2.

Cor. (B) *p* zu 2

Vl. *p*

p

Vla. *p*

Vc. Cb. *p*

Ob.
Cl.
Fg.
Cor. (B)
Vl.
Vla.
Vc. Cb.
230
Fl.
Ob.
Cl.
Fg.
Cor. (B)
Tr. (B)
Timp.
Vl.
Vla.
Vc. Cb.
zu 2

240
Fl.
Ob.
Cl.
Fg.
Cor. (B)
Tr. (B)
Timp
Vl.
Vla.
Vc. Cb.

Fl.
Ob.
Cl.
Fg.
Cor (B)
Tr. (B)
Timp.
Vl.
Vla
Vc. Cb.
sul G
sf
250
p
Vl.
Vla
Vc.

Fl.
Ob.
Cl.
Fg.
Cor. (B)
Tr. (B)
Timp.
Vl.
Vla.
Vc.
Cb.
sul G
260
cresc.

Fl.
Ob.
Cl.
Fg.
Cor. (B)
Tr. (B)
Timp.
Vl.
Vla.
Vc.
Cb.
ff
1.
tr

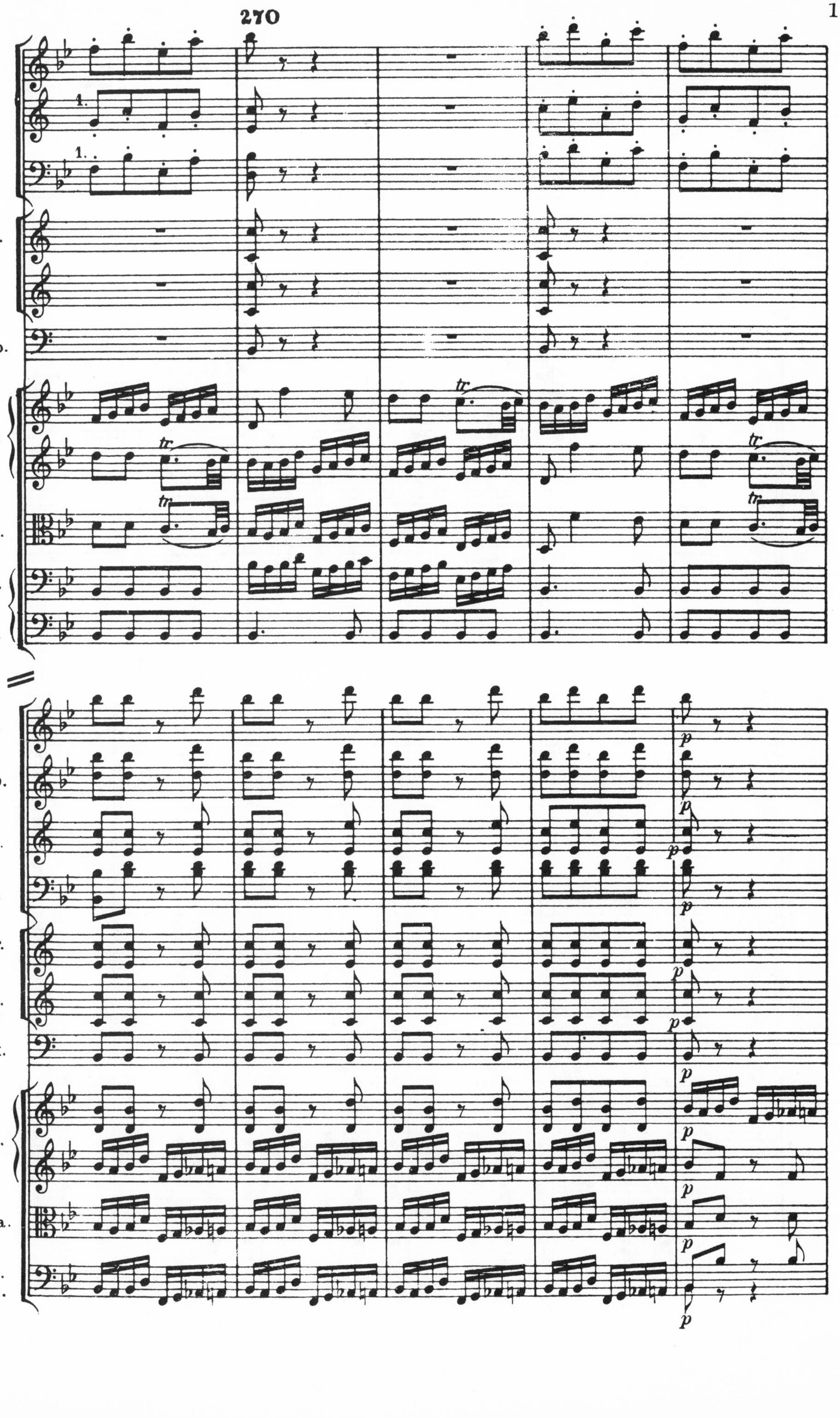
270
Fl.
Cl.
1.
Fg.
1.
Cor. (B)
Tr. (B)
Timp.
Vl.
tr
Vla.
Vc.
Cb.
Fl.
Ob.
Cl.
Fg.
Cor. (B)
Tr. (B)
Pk.
Vl.
Vla.
Vc. Cb.
p

280
Vl.
cresc.
cresc.
Vla.
cresc.
Vc.
cresc.
Vl.
Vla.
Vc.
290
Fl.
Ob.
Cl.
Fg.
Cor. (B)
Tr. (B)
Timp.
Vl.
Vla.
Vc.

Fl.
Ob.
Cl.
Fg.
Cor. (B)
Vl.
dim.
dim.
1.
dolce
zu 2
pp
pp
pp
pp
p
300
Tr. (B)
Timp.
Vla.
Vc.
Cb.
ff

310
Fl.
Ob.
Cl.
Fg.
Cor. (B)
Tr. (B)
Timp
Vl.
Vla.
Vc.
Cb.

Fl.
Ob.
Cl.
Fg.
zu 2
Cor (B)
Tr. (B)
Timp.
Vl.
Vla.
Vc.
Cb.
ff
sf
p
320
pp
Vc. Cb.

Fl.
Cl.
Fg.
Cor. (B)
Vl.
Vla
Vc. Cb
p
1.
pp
pp sempre
330
Ob.

Fl.
Ob.
Cl.
Fg.
Cor. (B)
Vl.
Vla.
Vc. Cb.
cresc.
f
340
Tr. (B)
Timp.
ff
zu 2
pp

350
Fl.
Ob.
Cl.
Fg.
zu 2
Cor.
(B)
Tr.
(B)
Timp.
Vl.
Vla
Vc.
Cb.
pp
ff

Symphony No.5

I

Allegro con brio (𝅗𝅥 = 108)

L. van Beethoven, Op. 67
1770 - 1827

20
Fl.
Ob.
Cl.
Fg.
Cor. (Es)
Tr. (C)
Tp.
Vl.
Vla.
Vc.
Cb.
p cresc.
cresc.
f
zu 2
30
ff
p
1.
Vc. Cb.

40
Fl.
Ob.
cresc.
Cl.
Fg.
cresc.
Cor. (Es)
Vl.
cresc.
cresc.
Vla.
cresc.
Vc. Cb.
cresc.
50
Fl.
Ob.
Cl.
Fg.
Cor. (Es)
Tr. (C)
Timp.
Vl.
Vla.
Vc. Cb.

Fl.
Ob.
Cl.
Fg.
Cor.
(Es)
Tr.
(C)
Timp.
Vl.
Vla.
Vc.
Cb.
60
zu 2
ff
sf
sf
sf
p
p dolce
p
p
70
1.
1.
p
p
p
p

80
1.
Ob.
Cl.
Fg.
Cor.
(Es)
Vl.
Vla.
Vc.
Cb.
p cresc.
cresc.
90
Fl.
Ob.
Cl.
Fg.
Cor.
(Es)
Tr.
(C)
Vl.
Vla
Vc.
Cb.
ff
zu 2

100
Fl.
Ob.
Cl.
Fg.
Cor. (Es)
Tr. (C)
Timp.
Vl.
Vla.
Vc. Cb
ff
f
110
zu 2
Fl.
Ob.
Cl.
Fg.
Cor. (Es)
Vl.
Vla.
Vc. Cb.

120
130
Fl.
Ob.
Cl.
Fg.
Cor.
(Es)
Vl.
Vla.
Vc.
Cb.
zu 2
ff
p
140

150
Cl.
Fg.
Cor. (Es)
Vl.
Vla.
Vc.
Cb.
cresc.
p
pizz.
Fl.
Ob
Tr. (C)
Timp.
zu 2
1.
pp
arco

160
Fl.
Ob.
Cl.
Fg.
Cor.
(Es)
Tr.
(C)
Timp.
Vl.
Vla.
Vc.
Cb.
cresc.
f

170
180
Fl.
Ob.
Cl.
Fg.
Cor.
(Es)
Tr.
(C)
Timp.
Vl.
Vla.
Vc.
Cb.
più f
ff
sf

190
Fl.
Ob.
Cl.
Fg.
Cor.
(Es)
zu 2
Tr.
(C)
zu 2
Timp.
Vl.
Vla.
Vc.
Cb.

zu 2
200
Fl.
Ob.
Cl.
Fg.
Cor. (Es)
Tr. (C)
Timp.
Vl.
Vla.
Vc. Cb.
ff
210
220
dimin.
p
pp
sempre più p
1
1.

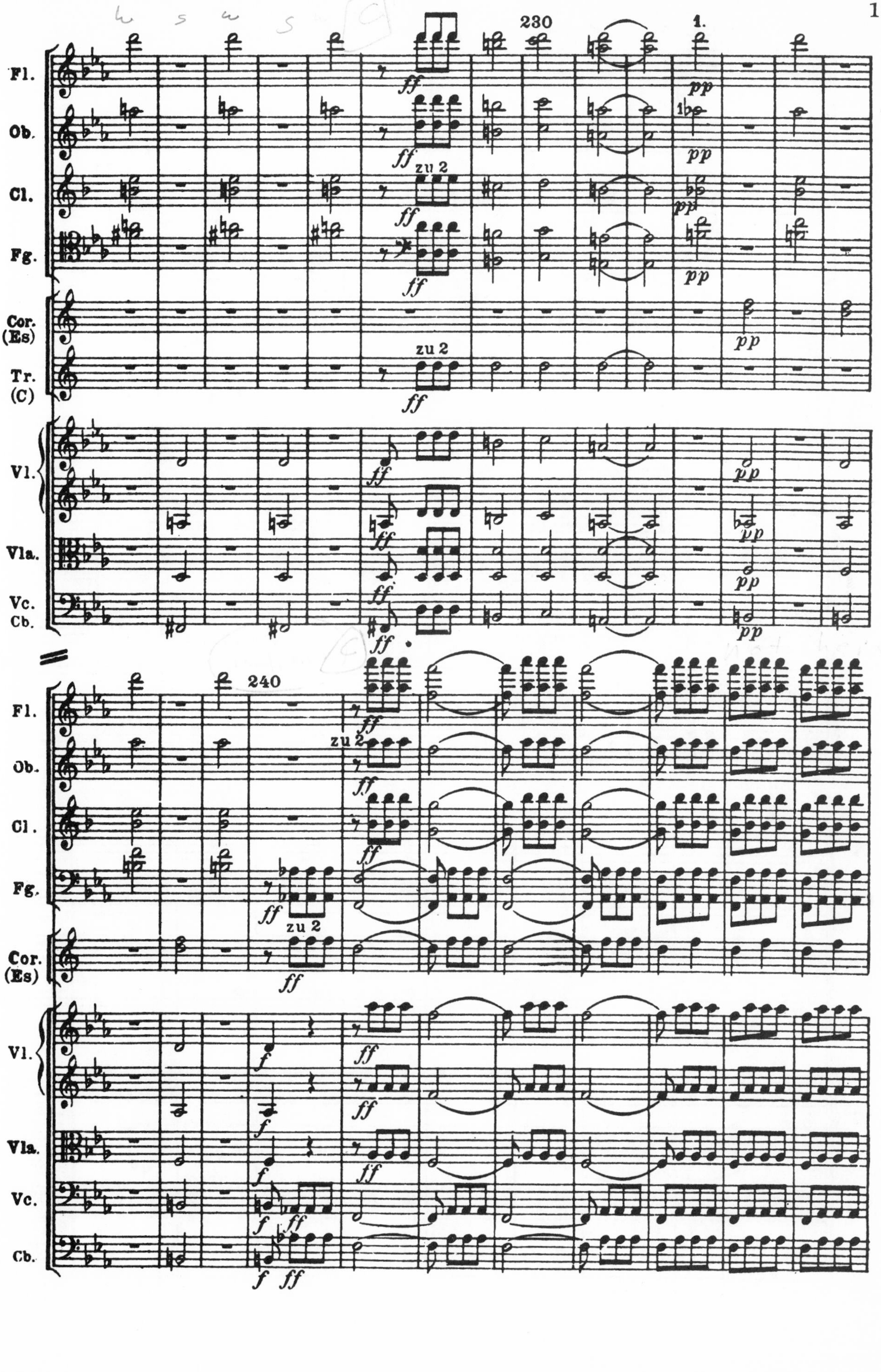

Fl.
Ob.
Cl.
Fg.
Cor. (Es)
Tr. (C)
Vl.
Vla.
Vc. Cb.

230
240

250
Fl.
Ob.
1.
p
Cl
p
Fg.
p
Cor.
(Es)
Tr.
(C)
ff
tr
Timp.
ff
ten.
ten.
Vl.
p
p
pizz.
Vla.
p
pizz.
Vc.
p
pizz.
Cb.
p
260
zu 2
Fl.
p
Ob.
cresc.
Cl.
Fg.
cresc.
Vl.
cresc.
cresc.
arco
Vla.
cresc.
Vc.
Cb.
cresc.

Adagio.
270
Fl.
Ob.
Cl.
Fg.
Cor. (Es)
Tr. (C)
Timp
Vl.
Vla.
Vc. Cb.
cresc.
arco
280
1.
Fl.
Ob.
Cl.
Fg.
Cor. (Es)
Tr. (C)
Timp.
Vl.
Vla.
Vc. Cb.

290
Fl.
Ob.
Cl.
Fg.
Cor. (Es)
Tr. (C)
Timp
Vl.
Vla.
Vc. Cb.
300
Fl.
Ob.
Cl.
Fg.
zu 2
Cor. (Es)
zu 2
Tr. (C)
Timp
Vl.
p dolce
Vla.
Vc. Cb.

310 1. 320

Fl.
p
Ob.
p
Fg.
Cor. (Es)
Timp
p
Vl.
Vla.
Vc. Cb.
p

330

Fl.
Ob.
Cl.
1.
p
Fg.
cresc.
Cor. (Es)
Timp.
Vl.
cresc.
cresc.
Vla.
cresc.
Vc.
cresc.
Cb.
cresc.

840
Fl.
Cl.
Fg.
Cor
(Es)
Vl.
Vla.
Vc.
Cb.
cresc.
cresc
zu 2
cresc.
350
Fl.
Ob.
Cl.
Fg.
Cor.
(Es)
Tr.
(C)
Timp.
Vl.
Vla.
Vc.
Cb.
ff
tr

360

zu 2

zu 2

Fl.

Ob.

Cl.

Fg.

zu 2

Cor. (Es)

Tr. (C)

Timp.

Vl.

Vla.

Vc. Cb.

370

Fl.

Ob.

Cl

Fg.

zu 2

Cor. (Es)

Tr. (C)

Timp.

Vl.

f

sf

Vla.

sf

Vc. Cb.

sf

380
Fl.
Ob.
Cl.
Fg.
(zu 2)
Cor.
(Es)
Tr.
(C)
Timp
Vl.
Vla.
Vc.
Cb.
sf
ff

390
Fl.
Ob.
Cl.
Fg.
Cor. (Es)
Tr. (C)
Timp.
Vl.
Vla.
Vc. Cb.
zu 2
p
ff

400
Fl.
Ob
Cl.
Fg.
Cor.
(Es)
Tr.
(C)
Timp.
Vl.
Vla.
Vc.
Cb.

1.
410
Fl.
Ob.
zu 2
Cl.
zu 2
Fg.
Cor. (Es)
zu 2.
Tr. (C)
Timp.
Vl.
Vla.
Vc.
Cb.

420
Fl.
Ob.
Cl.
Fg.
Cor.
(Es)
Tr.
(C)
Timp.
Vl.
Vla.
Vc.
Cb.
sf

430
440
Fl.
Ob.
Cl.
Fg.
Cor. (Es)
Tr. (C)
Timp.
Vl.
Vla.
Vc. Cb.
zu 2
ff

450
Fl.
Ob.
Cl.
Fg.
Cor. (Es)
Tr. (C)
Timp.
Vl.
Vla.
Vc.
Cb.

460
Fl.
Ob.
Cl.
Fg.
Cor. (Es)
Tr. (C)
Timp.
Vl.
Vla.
Vc. Cb.
sf

Fl.
470
Ob.
zu 2
Cl.
Fg.
Cor.
(Es)
zu 2
Tr.
(C)
Timp.
Vl.
Vla.
Vc.
Cb.
ff

480
490
Fl.
Ob.
Cl.
Fg.
Cor
(Es)
Tr.
(C)
Timp.
Vl.
Vla.
Vc.
Cb.
1.
p
pp
tr

500
Fl.
ff
Ob.
ff
Cl
ff
Fg.
ff
Cor.
(Es)
ff
Tr.
(C)
ff
Timp.
ff
Vl.
ff
ff
Vla.
ff
Vc.
ff
Cb.
ff

II

Andante con moto (♪ = 92)
2 Flauti
2 Oboi
2 Clarinetti in B
2 Fagotti
2 Corni in C
2 Trombe in C
Timpani in C-G
Violino I
Violino II
Viola
p dolce
f
Violoncello
p dolce
f
Contrabasso.
pizz.
p

10
1.
Fl.
Ob.
Cl.
Fg.
zu 2
cresc.
Vl.
Vla.
Vc.
arco
Cb.
20
dolce
p dolce
pizz.
Vc.
Cb.

Fl.
Ob.
Cl.
Fg.
Cor. (C)
Tr. (C)
Timp.
Vl.
Vla.
Vc.
Cb.

30

pp ff arco

Ob.
Cor. (C)
Tr. (C)
Timp.
Vl.
Vla.
Vc. Cb.

sempre ff sf tr

40
Ob.
Cl.
Fg.
Cor. (C)
Tr. (C)
Vl.
Vla.
Vc.
Cb.
p
pp
sempre pp
cresc.
f
pizz.
1.
50
dolce

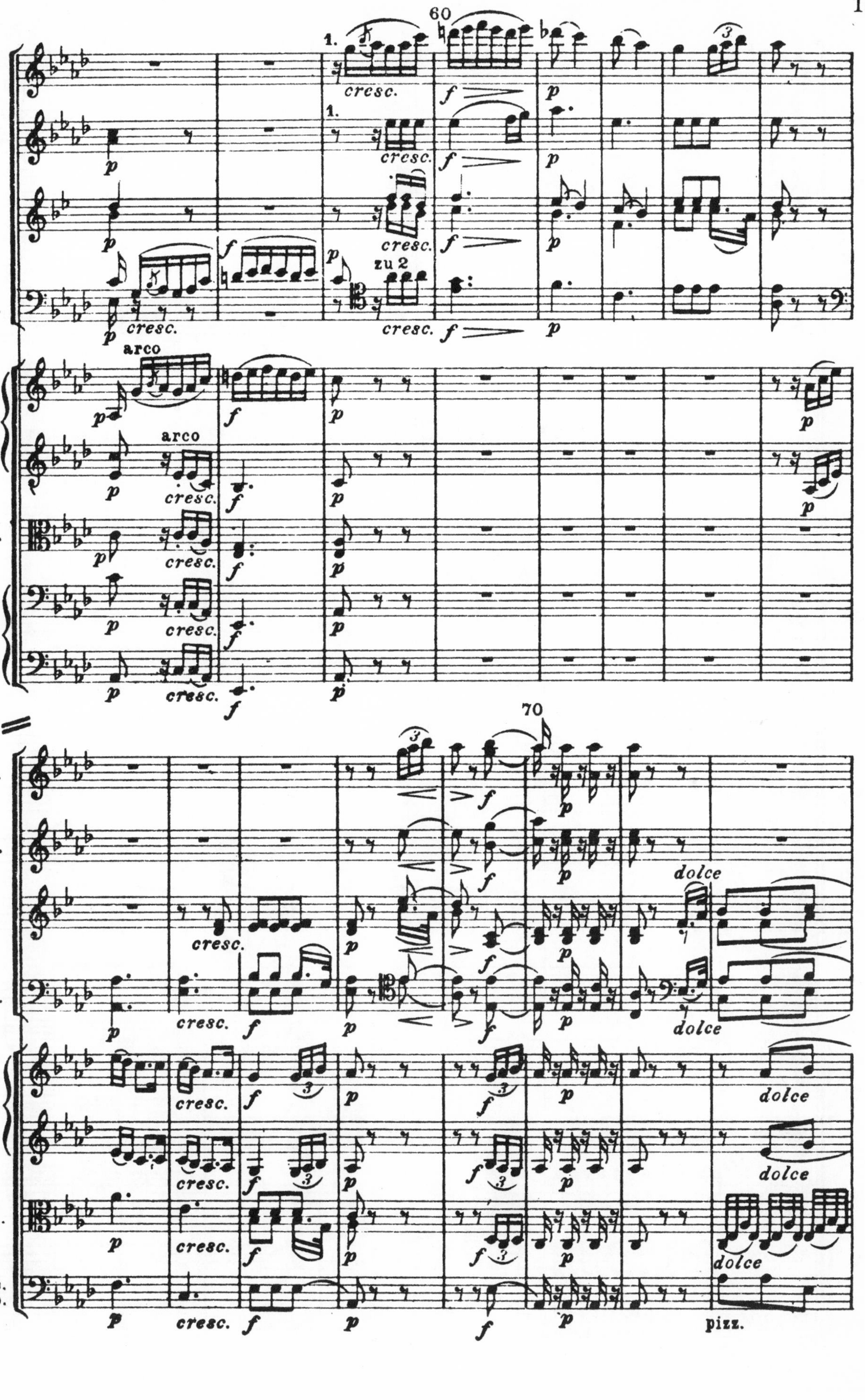

Fl.
Ob.
Cl.
Fg.
Vl.
Vla.
Vc.
Cb.
1.
pp
80
ff
Cor.
(C)
Tr.
(C)
Timp
arco
Vc.
Cb

Ob.
Cor. (C)
Tr. (C)
Timp.
Vl.
Vla.
Vc. Cb.
sf
f
Fg.
f dim.
p
pp
sempre pp
90
Vc.
Cb.

Fl.
Ob.
Cl.
Fg.
Vl.
Vla.
Vc.
Cb.
1.
zu 2
zu 2
ff
f
cresc.
100
pizz.
p
p dolce
1.

Fl.
Ob.
Fg.
pp
Vl.
Vla
Vc.
Cb.
Cl.
1.
p
arco
dolce
sempre pp
pizz.

110
Cl.
Fg.
Vl.
Vla.
Vc.
Cb.
Fl.
f
Ob.
Cl.
Fg.
zu 2
Cor.
(C)
Tr.
(C)
Timp.
Vl.
Vla.
arco
Vc.
Cb.
arco

120
Fl.
Ob.
Cl.
Fg.
zu 2
Cor. (C)
Tr. (C)
Timp.
Vl.
Vla.
Vc. Cb.
130
1.
dolce
pp
sempre pp
f

Fl.
Ob.
Cl
p
140
Fl.
cresc.
ff
Ob.
cresc.
ff
Cl.
cresc.
Fg.
ff
Cor.
(C)
f
ff
Tr.
(C)
ff
Timp.
ff
Vl.
p
ff
p
ff
Vla.
p
ff
Vc.
Cb.
p
ff

150
Fl.
Ob.
Cl.
Fg.
Cor. (C)
Tr. (C)
Timp.
Vl.
Vla.
Vc. Cb.
ff
dimin.
p
tr
pizz.
160
Vl.
Vla.
Vc.
Cb.
più p
pp
arco

Fl.
Ob.
Cl.
Fg.
Vl.
Vla
Vc.
Cb.
1.
p
pp
pizz.
170
Vc.
Cb.

cresc.
p dolce
Fl.
Ob.
f sf
Cl.
Fg.
Vl.
Vla.
Vc.
Cb.
f
1.
180
p dolce
arco
pp
cresc.

Fl.
Ob.
Cl.
Fg.
Cor. (C)
Tr. (C)
Timp
Vl.
Vla
Vc. Cb.
zu 2
1.
cresc.
ff

190
Fl.
Ob.
Cl.
Fg.
Cor.
(C)
Tr.
(C)
Timp.
Vl.
Vla
Vc.
Cb.

Fl.
Ob.
Cl.
Fg.
Cor. (C)
Tr. (C)
Timp.
Vl.
Vla.
Vc. Cb.

zu 2
zu 2
sf
sf
sf

Fl.
Ob.
Cl.
Fg.
Vl.
Vla
Vc. Cb.

200
1.
1.
zu 2
sf
p dolce
p dolce
p dolce
p dolce
p

Piu mosso. (♪= 116.)
Fl.
Cl.
Fg.
dolce
1.
pp
Vl.
Vla.
Vc.
Cb.
210
Ob.
Cor.
(C)
zu 2
p
f
cresc.

Tempo I.

Fl. Ob. Cl. Fg. Cor. (C) Tr. (C) Pk.

1. f ff p cresc. sf

Tempo I.

Vl. Br. Vc. Cb.

p cresc. f p cres ff

220

Fl. Ob. Cl. Fg.

p dolce cresc. sf f dolce

Vl. Vla. Vc. Cb.

p dolce cresc. f sf p pp

280

Cl. Fg. Vl. Vla. Vc. Cb.

cresc. f

240

Fl. Ob. Cl. Fg. Cor. (C) Tr. (C) Timp. Vl. Vla Vc. Cb.

zu 2

f ff sf p

III

Allegro (𝅗𝅥 = 96)
poco rit. a tempo
10
2 Flauti
2 Oboi
2 Clarinetti in B
2 Fagotti
2 Corni in Es
zu 2
2 Trombe in C
Timpani in C-G
Violino I
Violino II
Viola
Violoncello Contrabasso

poco rit.
1.
20
a tempo
Fl.
p
Cl.
1.
p
Fg.
1.
p
Cor. (Es)
zu 2
ff
Vl.
pp
f
pp
f
Vla
pp
f
Vc. Cb.
fp
f
zu 2
30
Fl.
f
Ob
f
Cl.
f
zu 2
Fg.
f
Cor. (Es)
zu 2
Vl.
f
f
Vla.
f
Vc. Cb.
f

40
Fl.
Ob.
Cl.
Fg.
Cor. (Es)
Vl.
Vla
Vc. Cb.
sf
zu 2
dimin. pp
2.
p
pp
poco rit.
a tempo
50
60
1.
Vla.

70
Ob.
cresc.
Cl.
cresc.
Cor.
(Es)
cresc.
Vl.
pp
cresc.
pp
cresc.
Vla.
cresc.
Vc.
Cb.
cresc.
1.
zu 2
80
Fl.
f
ff
Ob.
zu 2
f
ff
Cl.
f
ff
Fg.
zu 2
f
ff
zu 2
Cor.
(Es)
f
Tr.
(C)
f
Timp.
f
Vl.
f
f
Vla.
f
Vc.
Cb.
f

90
Fl.
Ob.
zu 2
Cl.
Fg.
Cor. (Es)
Tr. (C)
Timp.
Vl.
Vla.
Vc. Cb.
ff
sf

100
1.
Fl.
sf
sf
dimin. pp
p
Ob.
Cl.
Fg.
zu 2
Cor. (Es)
Tr. (C)
pdimin. pp
Timp.
Vl.
Vla.
Vc.
Cb.

Fl.
Ob.
Cl.
Fg.
Cor. (Es)
Timp.
Vl.
Vla.
Vc.
Cb.
110
120
p
zu 2
arco
pizz.
pp
sempre p
cresc.

Fl.
Ob.
Cl.
Fg.
Cor. (Es)
Tr. (C)
Timp.
Vl.
Vla.
Vc.
Cb.
130
p
cresc.
f
arco

140
Fl.
Ob.
Cl.
Fg.
Cor (Es)
Tr. (C)
Timp.
Vl.
Vla.
Vc. Cb.
ff
p
1.
zu 2
Fg.
Vla.
Vc. Cb.
zu 2
f

150
Fl.
Ob.
Fg.
Cor.
(Es)
Timp.
Vl.
Vla.
Vc.
Cb.
1.
2.
160
Tr.
(C)

170
zu 2
Cl.
Fg.
Vla.
Vc.
Cb.
180
Fl.
Ob.
Cor.
(Es)
Tr.
(C)
Timp.
Vl.

Fl.
Ob.
Cl.
Fg.
zu 2
Cor. (Es)
Tr. (C)
Timp.
Vl.
Vla.
Vc.
Cb.

190
zu 2
Fl.
Ob.
Cl.
Fg.
Cor.
(Es)
Tr.
(C)
Timp.
Vl.
ff
Vla
ff
Vc.
Cb.
200
2. Vl.
Vla.
Vc.
f
dimin.
p

Cl.
Vla.
Vc.
Cb.
1.
210
p
sempre più p
Fl.
Ob.
Fg.
Vl.
pp
sempre pp
220
230

240

Cl.
Fg.
Cor. (Es)
Vc. Cb.

pizz. *p* arco *pp* *pp* *pp* *pp*

poco ritard. a tempo

250

Cl.
Fg.
Cor. (Es)
Vl.
Vla.
Vc.
Cb.

zu 2 *p* pizz. *p* pizz. *p* pizz. *p* pizz. *p*

poco ritard. a tempo

260

Cl.
Fg.
Vl.
Vla.
Vc.

zu 2 *pp* *pp* arco *sempre pp* pizz. *pp* *pp* arco *sempre pp* *pp*

1.
270
Ob.
pp
Fg.
pp
sempre pp
Vl.
pizz.
pp
sempre pp
sempre pp
Vla.
pizz.
arco
sempre pp
Vc.
sempre pp
Fg.
280
Vl.
Vla.
Vc.
290
Ob.
p
p
Fg.
pp
Cor.
(Es)
1.
p
Vl.
sempre pp
sempre pp
Vla.
pp
sempre pp
Vc.
sempre pp

Fg.
Cor. (Es)
Vl.
Vla.
Vc.
1.
800
p
810
320
pp
pizz.
arco

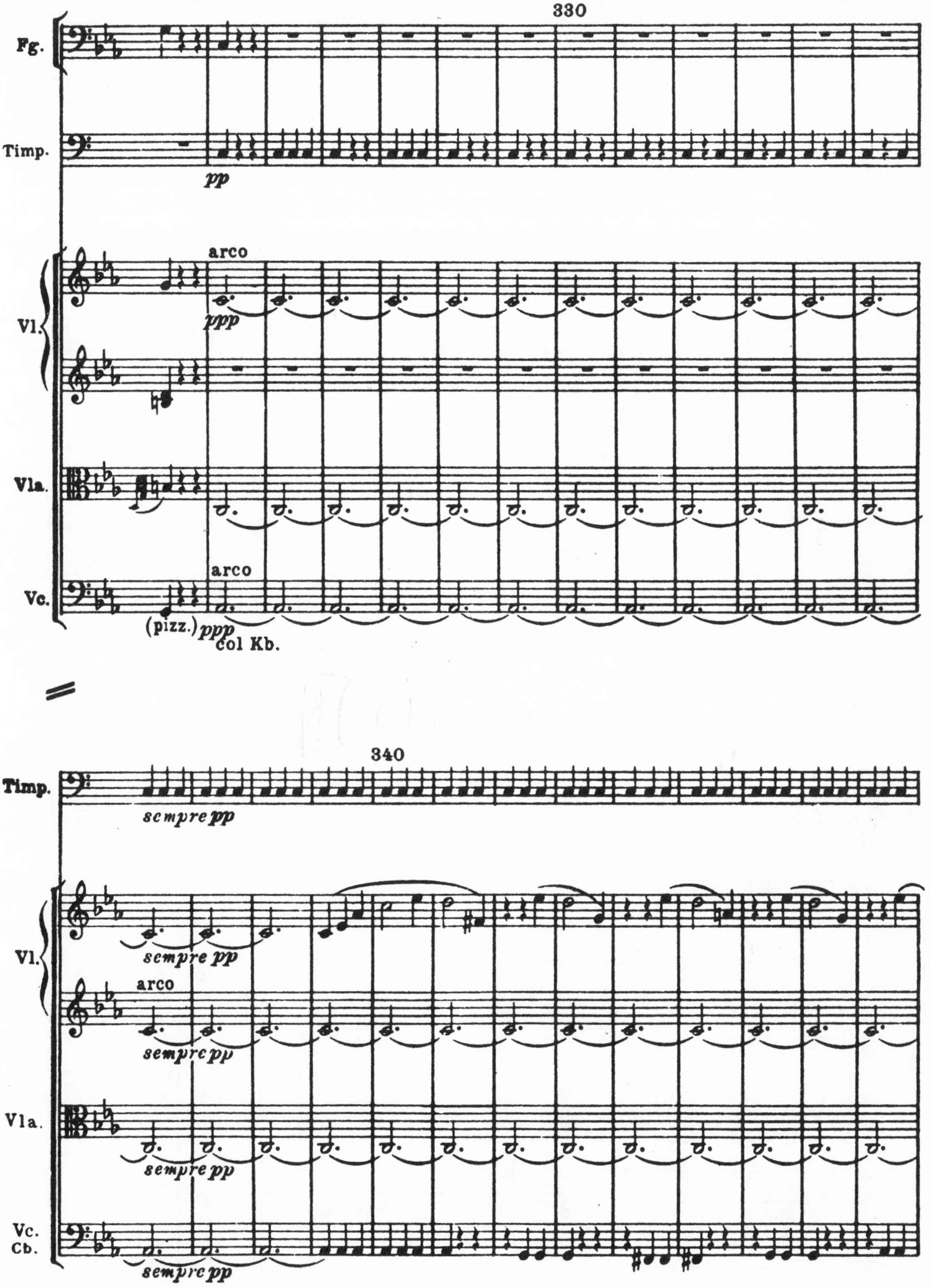

330

Fg.

Timp.

pp

arco

Vl.

ppp

Vla.

arco

Vc.

(pizz.) *ppp*

col Kb.

350
360
Timp.
Vl.
Vla
Vc.
Cb.
370
Fl.
p cresc.
Ob.
pp cresc.
Fg.
pp cresc.
in C
Cor.
(C)
p cresc.
Tr.
(C)
p cresc.
Timp.
cresc.
Vl.
cresc.
cresc.
Vla.
cresc.
Vc.
Cb.
cresc.
Attacca:

IV

Allegro (𝅗𝅥 = 84)
Piccolo
2 Flauti
2 Oboi
2 Clarinetti in C
2 Fagotti
zu 2
Contrafagotto
2 Corni in C
2 Trombe in C
Alto
Tenore
3 Tromboni
Basso
Timpani in C-G
Violino I
Violino II
Viola
Violoncello
Contrabasso
ff

10
Picc.
Fl.
zu 2
Ob.
zu 2
Cl.
Fg.
Cfg.
Cor. (C)
Tr. (C)
Tbni.
Timp.
Vl.
Vla.
Vc. Cb.

Picc.
Fl.
Ob.
Cl.
Fg.
Cfg.
Cor.
(C)
Tr.
(C)
Tbni.
Timp.
Vl.
Vla.
Vc.
Cb.

20
Picc.
Fl.
Ob.
zu 2
Cl.
Fg.
Cfg.
Cor.
(C)
Tr.
(C)
Toni.
Timp.
Vl.
Vla.
Vc.
Cb.

Picc.
Fl.
Ob.
Cl.
zu 2
Fg.
zu 2
Cfg.
Cor.
(C)
Tr.
(C)
Tbni.
Timp.
Vl.
Vla.
Vc.
Cb.

80
Picc.
Fl.
Ob.
Cl.
Fg.
Cfg.
Cor.
(C)
Tr.
(C)
Tbni
Timp.
Vl.
Vla.
Vc.
Cb.

Fl.
Ob.
Cl.
Fg.
Cfg.
zu 2
Cor. (C)
zu 2
Tr. (C)
Tbni.
Timp.
Vl.
Vla.
Vc. Cb.

40
zu 2
1.
Fl.
ff
Ob.
Cl.
Fg.
Cfg.
Cor.
(C)
Tr.
(C)
Tbni.
Vl.
Vla.
Vc.
Cb.

Picc.
Fl.
Ob.
Cl.
Fg.
Cfg.
Cor. (C)
Tr. (C)
Timp.
Vl.
Vla.
Vc.
Cb.
f
cresc.
p
zu 2
3

50
Picc
Fl.
Ob.
Cl.
Fg.
Cfg.
Cor. (C)
Tr. (C)
Tbni.
Timp.
Vl.
Vla.
Vc.
Cb.

Fl.
Ob.
Cl.
Fg.
Cfg.
Cor. (C)
Tr. (C)
Tbni.
Timp.
Vl.
Vla
Vc.
Cb.
pp
cresc.
ff
zu 2
f
dolce

60
Fl.
Ob.
zu 2
Cl.
Fg.
Cfg.
Cor
(C)
Tr.
(C)
Tbni.
Timp.
Vl.
Vla.
Vc.
Cb.

Fl.
Ob.
Cl.
Fg.
Cfg.
Cor. (C)
Tr. (C)
Tbni.
Timp.
Vl.
Vla
Vc.
Cb.
fp
p
sf

70
Picc.
Fl.
Ob.
Cl.
Fg.
Cfg.
Cor.
(C)
Tr.
(C)
Tbni.
Timp.
Vl.
Vla.
Vc.
Cb.
1.
p dolce
1.
zu 2
zu 2
zu 2
zu 2
f
p

80
Picc.
Fl.
Ob.
Cl.
Fg.
Cfg.
Cor. (C)
Tr. (C)
Tbni.
Timp.
Vl.
Vla.
Vc. Cb.
sf
più f
ff
zu 2

1.
Picc.
Fl.
Ob.
zu 2
Cl.
Fg.
zu 2
Cfg.
Cor.
(C)
Tr.
(C)
Tbni.
Timp.
Vl.
Vla.
Vc.
Cb.

2.
Picc.
zu 2
Fl.
zu 2
Ob.
Cl.
zu 2
Fg.
Cfg.
Cor. (C)
Tr. (C)
Tbni.
Timp.
Vl.
Vla.
Vc. Cb.
zu 2
zu 2
zu 2

90
Picc.
Fl.
Ob.
Cl.
Fg.
Cfg.
Cor.
(C)
zu 2
Tr.
(C)
Tbni.
Vl.
Vla.
Vc.
Cb.
p

1.
Fl.
1.
p
Ob.
dolce
Cor.
(C)
p
Vl.
Vla.
Vc.

dolce
100
1.
Fl.
p
1.
Ob.
p
1.
Cl.
p
1.
1.
Fg.
p
p
zu 2
Cor.
(C)
p
Vl.
Vla.
Vc.

Fl.
Ob.
Cl.
Fg.
Cfg.
Vl.
Vla.
Vc.
Kb.

Fl.
Ob.
Cl.
zu 2
Fg.
ff
Cfg.
zu 2
Cor.
(C)
f
Tr.
(C)
f
zu 2
f
Tbni.
tr
Timp.
f
Vl.
Vla.
Vc.
Cb.

zu 2
120
Fl.
zu 2
Ob.
Cl.
zu 2
Fg.
Cfg.
Cor.
(C)
zu 2
Tr.
(C)
Trbni
Timp.
Vl.
Vla.
Vc.
Cb.

Fl.
più f
Ob.
più f
zu 2
Cl.
più f
zu 2
Fg.
più f
zu 2
Cfg.
più f
Cor.
(C)
più f
Tr.
(C)
più f
Tbni.
più f
più f
Timp.
più f
Vl.
più f
più f
Vla.
più f
Vc.
più f
Cb.
più f

Fl.
Ob.
Cl.
Fg.
Cfg.
Cor. (C)
Tr. (C)
Tbni.
Timp.
Vl.
Vla.
Vc. Cb.
130
1.
zu 2
zu 2
zu 2
zu 2

Picc.
Fl.
Ob.
Cl.
zu 2
Fg.
Cfg.
Cor.
(C)
Tr.
(C)
Tbni
Timp.
Vl.
Vla.
Vc.
Cb.
ff

Picc.
Fl.
Ob.
Cl.
Fg.
Cfg.
Cor.
(C)
Tr.
(C)
Tbni.
Timp.
Vl.
Vla.
Vc.
Cb.

140
Picc.
Fl.
Ob.
Cl.
Fg.
Cfg.
Cor.
(C)
Tr.
(C)
Tbni.
Timp.
Vl.
Vla.
Vc.
Cb.
sf
sempre ff
tr

Picc.
Fl.
Ob.
Cl.
Fg.
Cfg.
Cor.
(C)
Tr.
(C)
Tbni.
Timp.
Vl.
Vla.
Vc.
Cb.

150
Tempo I. (𝅗𝅥. = 96.)
160
Picc.
Fl.
Ob.
Cl.
Fg.
Cfg.
Cor. (C)
Tr. (C)
Tbni.
Timp.
Vl.
dimin.
pp
Vla.
Vc. Cb.

170
1
Ob.
Cl.
p
pizz.
arco
pizz.
Vl.
pizz.
pp
pizz.
Vla
pp
Vc.
pp
180
Ob
Cl.
Cor.
(C)
pp
pp
Vl.
arco
Vla.
Vc.

190
1.
Fl.
p dolce
Ob.
Cl.
1.
Fg.
p dolce
Cor
(C)
Vla.
200
Fl.
cresc.
Ob.
cresc.
Cl.
cresc.
Fg.
cresc.
Cor.
(C)
cresc.
Timp.
pp
cresc.
arco
Vl.
cresc.
arco
cresc.
Vla
cresc.
arco
Vc.
Cb.
cresc.

Allegro. (𝅗𝅥 = 84)
210
Picc.
Fl.
Ob.
Cl.
Fg.
Cfg.
Cor. (C)
Tr. (C)
Tbni.
Timp.
Vl.
Vla.
Vc.
Cb.
ff
zu 2

Picc.
Fl.
Ob.
Cl.
Fg.
Cfg.
Cor. (C)
Tr. (C)
Tbni.
Timp.
Vl.
Vla.
Vc. Cb.

220
Picc.
Fl.
Ob.
Cl.
Fg.
Cfg.
Cor
(C)
Tr.
(C)
Tbni.
Timp.
Vl.
Vla.
Vc.
Cb.

Picc.
Fl.
Ob.
zu 2
Cl.
Fg.
Cfg.
Cor.
(C)
Tr.
(C)
Tbni.
Timp.
Vl.
Vla.
Vc.
Cb

230
Picc.
Fl.
Ob.
Cl.
zu 2
Fg.
zu 2
Cfg.
Cor.
(C)
Tr.
(C)
Tbni.
Timp.
Vl.
Vla.
Vc.
Cb.

Fl.
Ob.
Cl.
Fg.
C fg.
Cor. (C)
Tr. (C)
Tbni.
Timp.
Vl.
Vla.
Vc. Cb.

240
Picc.
Fl.
zu 2
Ob.
zu 2
Cl.
Fg.
zu 2
Cfg.
Cor.
(C)
Tr.
(C)
Tbni.
Timp.
Vl.
Vla.
Vc.
Cb.

250
Picc.
Fl.
Ob.
Cl.
zu 2
Fg.
Cfg.
Cor.
(C)
Tr.
(C)
Tbni.
Timp.
Vl.
Vla.
Vc.
Cb.

Fl.
Ob.
Cl.
Fg.
Cfg.
Cor.
(C)
Tr.
(C)
Tbni.
Timp.
Vl.
Vla.
Vc.
Cb.
p

260
Picc.
Fl.
Ob.
Cl.
Fg.
Cfg.
Cor. (C)
Tr. (C)
Tbni.
Timp.
Vl.
Vla.
Vc.
Cb.
cresc.
p dolce
1.

Fl.
Ob.
Cl.
Fg.
Cfg.
Cor (C)
Tr. (C)
Tbni.
Timp.
Vl.
Vla.
Vc.
Cb.
1.
pp
cresc.
ff
p dolce
p
f
Vl.

270
Picc.
Fl.
zu 2
Ob.
zu 2
Cl.
zu 2
Fg.
Cfg.
Cor.
(C)
Tr.
(C)
Tbni.
Timp.
Vl.
Vla.
Vc.
Cb

Picc.
Fl.
1.
p dolce
Ob.
1.
fp dolce
fp
fp
Cl.
fp dolce
fp
Fg.
fp dolce
fp
fp
Cfg.
Cor.
(C)
p dolce
fp
Tr.
(C)
Timp.
Vl.
p
p
f
p
fp
fp
fp
Vla.
f
fp
fp
Vc.
Cb.

280
zu 2
Fl.
Ob.
Cl.
Fg.
Cfg.
Cor. (C)
Tr. (C)
Tbni.
Timp.
Vl.
Vla.
Vc. Cb.

290
Fl.
Ob.
Cl.
Fg.
Cfg.
Cor (C)
Tr. (C)
Tbni.
Timp.
Vl.
Vla.
Vc. Cb.
sf
più f
ff
tr

Fl.
Ob.
Cl.
Fg.
C.fg.
Cor
(C)
Tr.
(C)
Tbni.
Timp.
Vl.
Vla.
Vc.
Cb.
sf
f
1.

300
1.
Fl.
più f
Ob.
Cl.
Fg.
Cfg.
sf
Cor.
(C)
Tr.
(C)
Tbni.
Timp
Vl.
Vla.
Vc.
Cb.

Fl.
Ob.
Cl.
zu 2
Fg.
Cfg.
Cor. (C)
Tr. (C)
Tbni.
Timp.
Vl.
Vla.
Vc. Cb.
ff
sf

310
Fl.
Ob.
Cl.
Fg.
C.fg.
Cor.
(C)
Tr.
(C)
Tbni.
Timp.
Vl.
sf
sf
sf
sf
sf
sf
Vla.
sf
sf
sf
Vc.
Cb.

320
Fl.
1.
p dolce cresc. poco a poco
Ob.
Cl.
1.
p cresc. poco a poco
Fg.
zu 2
ff
1.
p
cresc.
Cfg.
Cor.
(C)
zu 2
p dolce
cresc. poco a poco
Tr.
(C)
Tbni.
Timp.
Vl.
p cresc. poco a poco
Vla.
p cresc. poco a poco
Vc.
Cb.

Picc.
Fl.
Ob.
Cl.
Fg.
Cfg.
Cor. (C)
Tr. (C)
Tbni.
Timp.
Vl.
Vla.
Vc.
Cb.
p cresc.
f
1.
tr
p cresc. poco a poco
cresc.

330
Picc.
Fl.
Ob.
Cl.
Fg.
Cfg.
Cor.
(C)
Tr.
(C)
Tbni.
Timp.
Vl.
Vla.
Vc.
Cb.
p
f

340
Picc.
p dolce
cresc. poco a poco
Fl.
p cresc. poco a poco
p cresc.
Ob.
p dolce
p cresc. poco a poco
Fg.
p cresc.
Cfg.
zu 2
Cor. (C)
p dolce
cresc. poco a poco
Vl.
p cresc. poco a poco
p cresc. poco a poco
Vla.
p cresc. poco a poco
Vc.
p cresc. poco a poco
Cb.
p cresc.

Picc.
Fl.
zu 2
Ob.
Cl.
cresc.
Fg.
Cfg.
Cor. (C)
Tr. (C)
p cresc.
Tbni.
Timp.
p cresc.
Vl.
Vla
Vc.
Cb.

350
Sempre
Picc
Fl.
Ob.
Cl.
Fg.
Cfg.
Cor. (C)
Tr. (C)
Tbni.
Timp.
Vl.
Vla.
Vc. Cb.
p
cresc. poco a poco
1.
zu 2

più allegro
360
Presto (𝅝 = 112.)
Picc.
Fl.
Ob.
Cl.
Fg.
Cfg.
Cor. (C)
Tr. (C)
Timp.
Vl.
Vla.
Vc. Cb
f
zu 2
p
cresc.
fp

870
Fl.
Ob.
Cl.
Fg.
Cfg.
Cor. (C)
Tr. (C)
Timp.
Vl.
Vla.
Vc. Cb.

380
Fl.
fp
fp
cresc.
Ob.
fp
fp
cresc.
Cl.
fp
fp
cresc.
Fg.
fp
fp
cresc.
Cfg.
fp
fp
cresc.
Cor. (C)
f
fp
cresc.
Tp. (C)
f
f
p cresc.
Timp.
f
f
p cresc.
Vl.
fp
fp
cresc.
fp
fp
cresc.
Vla.
fp
fp
cresc.
Vc. Cb.
fp
fp
cresc.

390
Picc.
cresc.
f
ff
Fl.
zu 2
Ob.
Cl.
Fg.
Cfg.
Cor. (C)
Tr. (C)
Tbni.
Timp.
Vl.
Vla.
Vc. Cb.

Picc.
Fl.
Ob.
Cl.
Fg.
zu 2
C fg.
Cor.
(C)
zu 2
Tr.
(C)
zu 2
Timp.
Vl.
Vla.
Vc.
Cb.

400
Picc.
Fl.
Ob.
zu 2
Cl.
zu 2
Fg.
C.fg.
Cor (C)
Tr. (C)
Timp.
tr
Vl.
Vla.
Vc. Cb.

410
Picc.
sempre ff
Fl.
sempre ff
Ob.
sempre ff
Cl.
sempre ff
Fg.
sempre ff
C fg.
sempre ff
Cor. (C)
sempre ff
Tr. (C)
sempre ff
Tbni.
sempre ff
sempre ff
Timp.
sempre ff
Vl.
sempre ff
sempre ff
Vla.
sempre ff
Vc. Cb.
sempre ff

420
Picc
Fl.
zu 2
Ob.
zu 2
Cl.
zu 2
Fg.
Cfg.
Cor. (C)
zu 2
Tr. (C)
Tbni.
Timp.
Vl.
Vla.
Vc. Cb.

430
Picc.
Fl.
Ob.
Cl.
Fg.
Cfg.
Cor.
(C)
Tr.
(C)
Tbni.
Timp.
Vl.
Vla.
Vc.
Cb.

440
Picc.
Fl.
Ob.
Cl.
zu 2
Fg.
Cfg.
Cor.
(C)
Tr.
(C)
Tbni.
Timp.
Vl.
Vla.
Vc.
Cb.